ONESIMPLEWORD
WORKBOOK

Todd A. Sinelli

ONESIMPLEWORD Workbook
Copyright © 2013 by Todd A. Sinelli

www.littorch.com

Designed by Alexandra Rearick.
Author photo by Sudha Mathai Photography.
Written by Todd A. Sinelli.
Inspired by Jesus.
Published by Lit Torch Publishing, Dallas, Texas.

ISBN: 188735705X / 978-1-887357-05-0
Printed in the United States of America.
First edition, 2013
1 2 3 4 5 6 7 — 18 17 16 15 14 13

Also by Todd A. Sinelli

Evolution Within | One Lit Torch | True Riches | One Simple Word

So that, just as it is written, "Let him who boast, boast in the Lord."

1 Corinthians 1:31 (NASB)

TABLE OF CONTENTS

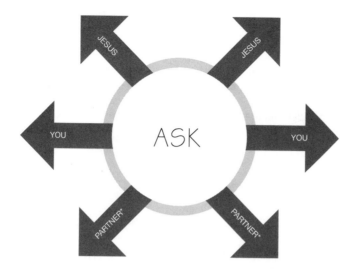

One Simple Word: **ASK**

What do you think it would be like to be in a relationship with someone who never asked you a question?

A relationship with Jesus is not like that. Jesus asks questions, a lot of questions, such as, "What are you seeking?" (John 1:38) "Why are you so afraid?" (Mark 4:40) "Do you love me?" (John 21:17) and "Do you wish to get well?" (John 5:6). There are over 300 questions Jesus asks in the New Testament and the fascinating thing is He doesn't have to ask anyone anything.[1]

Jesus is God and knows everything; however, He graciously brings people into a relationship through the questions He asks.

Many of us want relationships. We long for enduring relationships. And the great thing about Jesus is that He has designed a relationship with Him to last a long, long time. You probably discovered that the quality of a relationship without questions and conversation will drift, diminish and ultimately fade over time. This also applies to our relationship with God and to others.

Do you have a relationship right now with someone who rarely asks you a question? How enjoyable is that?

A surprising insight for you may be that the Bible is a constant series of conversations. Throughout Scripture God is frequently talking with or to someone and the Bible is designed to help us communicate with God and with others. The Lord has provided the perfect model for conversation and community through the example in His Son, Jesus Christ.

Jesus spoke with men, women, kids, kings and lives were forever changed after a conversation with Him. His questions cause us to consider our life in light of our present situations and the reality of our eternal destination. His questions challenge, comfort and change us. His questions draw us near, open us up and bring us into the realization that we were designed for relationships first with Him and then with others.

> **John 17:21 (NASB)** That they may all be one; even as You, Father, are in Me and I in You, that they also may be in Us, so that the world may believe that You sent Me.

INTRODUCTION

In the Bible we are only given a glimpse into about 45 days of Jesus' life.[2] Some two thousand years later, we are still challenged by His words, His actions and more specifically, by His questions.

It is a remarkable thought to consider that the Creator of the universe has designed us for a relationship with Him. And to engage us in this relationship, He uses conversation and the application of this one simple word—ask.

Step 1| Imagine

Imagine what could happen if you were to develop the skill of asking questions.

In the book How to Be Twice as Smart, Scott Witt writes, "Be inquisitive. Never be satisfied with mere facts; seek to learn reasons as well. Develop the habit of asking questions—of yourself as well as others—even when the topic is not immediately important to you. It's not the knowledge you'll gain that counts, but rather the strengthening of your curiosity. The curiosity of most adults has withered. Isn't it time you rebuilt yours?"[3]

Ask. Ask God. Ask yourself. Ask others. Ask is a verb, it is an action, and it is a life-changing concept. Humility, wonder, and curiosity grow stronger as we listen and ask questions.

> Jesus said, "If you abide in Me, and My words abide in you, ask whatever you wish, and it will be done for you. My Father is glorified by this, that you bear much fruit, and so prove to be My disciples" **(John 15:7-8 NAS)**.

Through this workbook, you will explore three ways questions are asked in the Bible. There are questions God asks us, questions we ask God and questions we ask one another. Each week you will explore all three. In week one, you will interact with Jesus' most frequently asked question. Week two will have you exploring the first question ever asked. In week three you will learn one question to avoid in relationships and finish with one question everyone must answer in week four.

Ultimately, this workbook was designed to help you do two things:
1| Talk with Jesus
2| Talk with others about Jesus using one simple word.

By starting immediately, significant rewards await you:
1| The reward of knowing God and others more deeply. God promises to reward you as you draw near to Him.

James 4:8 (NASB) Draw near to God and He will draw near to you.

Hebrews 11:6 (NIV) And without faith it is impossible to please God, because anyone who comes to him must believe that he exists and that he rewards those who earnestly seek him.

2| The reward of connecting and conversing with God. You have the opportunity to ask and receive help from the Creator of the universe in the days ahead.

Hebrews 4:16 (NIV) Let us then approach the throne of grace with confidence, so that we may receive mercy and find grace to help us in our time of need.

Matthew 7:11 (NIV) If you, then, though you are evil, know how to give good gifts to your children, how much more will your Father in heaven give good gifts to those who ask him!

3| Rewards beyond compare. There are blessings beyond what you could ask or even imagine waiting for you as your understanding and relationship with Jesus and others grow.

Ephesians 3:20-21 (NIV) Now to him who is able to do immeasurably more than all we ask or imagine, according to his power that is at work within us, to him be glory in the church and in Christ Jesus throughout all generations, for ever and ever! Amen.

Hebrews 6:9 (NASB) But, beloved, we are convinced of better things concerning you, and things that accompany salvation, though we are speaking in this way.

Time spent drawing closer to God has no downside. However, by not accepting the invitation to draw near to the Lord, there may be some regrets.

1| The regret of being unconnected from Jesus and others with the fear of remaining this way.

2| The regret of maintaining a superficial or a fading relationship and failing to understand the impact and significance of this one simple word.

3 | The regret that may linger the longest will be from not asking to receive mercy and grace in a time of need from God and from others.

We are all at different places in our journey with Christ. You may have been walking with Jesus nearly every day or you may be just beginning a relationship with Him. You may know your Bible very well or you may not. You may feel comfortable going to church or you may not have been there for a while. Wherever you are, that is okay, God meets us where we are.

Step 2| One Thing is Needed

As you begin this workbook, one thing that you will need is a partner. This could be a new friend, an old friend, your spouse, son, daughter, niece, nephew, co-worker, boyfriend, girlfriend, fellow student, or neighbor. You can do this study within a small group; however, each person must be matched with a partner.

When Jesus sent out His disciples, He paired them up two by two (Mark 6:7). This workbook follows that same instruction and therefore, pairing up will prove immensely valuable. You might be tempted to work through this study alone. Please don't.

Let me be clear, having a partner is a critical part of this study as this workbook was designed to bring people together like Jesus did. At least two people are needed to have a conversation following the model Scriptures provides.

Luke 10:1-2 (NIV) After this the Lord appointed seventy-two others and sent them two by two ahead of him to every town and place where he was about to go. He told them, "The harvest is plentiful, but the workers are few. Ask the Lord of the harvest, therefore, to send out workers into his harvest field."

Some think you need to become a pastor, priest, nun or Bible scholar to really be close to God; this is not true. Jesus welcomes and invites all people to be with Him. Can you think of a group in the Bible who were not pastors, priests or Bible scholars? Hint, most of them were fisherman.

To converse with Jesus and to converse with others about Jesus is a privilege that many religious people in the Bible missed. They even complained and muttered as they watched Jesus welcome and dine with people they thought were below them.

> **Luke 15:1-2 (NIV)** Now the tax collectors and "sinners" were all gathering around to hear him. But the Pharisees and the teachers of the law muttered, "This man welcomes sinners and eats with them."

> **Mark 3:14 (NASB)** And He appointed twelve, so that they would be with Him and that He could send them out to preach.

The Bible says, "two are better than one because they will have a good return for their labor" (Ecclesiastes 4:9). There will be a reward for you and your partner. God has promised to reward those who earnestly seek Him (Hebrews 11:6). You can trust God to keep His promises to you.

Ask God to help you select a partner whom you can learn from and who can learn from you as well over the next four weeks.

> **Hebrews 10:24-25 (NIV)** And let us consider how we may spur one another on toward love and good deeds. Let us not give up meeting together, as some are in the habit of doing, but let us encourage one another--and all the more as you see the Day approaching.

Right now, go ahead and ask God who should join you in this study. Ask the Lord to help you select someone that will be an encourager during this time. "Lord, who should I ask to be my partner?" Begin by writing a few names that come to mind:

Person 1|

Person 2|

Person 3|

Asking the Lord to help you match up with a partner is an important first step. Remember, even if you are doing this within a small group, each person is to have a partner.

You will soon discover that this workbook is filled with Scripture and the Bible says it is God, His words and His Spirit that will build you up and perform a good work in you as you discover the simplicity and importance of this one simple word — ask.

> **Acts 20:32 (NIV)** Now I commit you to God and to the word of his grace, which can build you up and give you an inheritance among all those who are sanctified.

> **John 6:63 (NIV)** The Spirit gives life; the flesh counts for nothing. The words I have spoken to you are spirit and they are life.

> **Philippians 1:6 (NASB)** For I am confident of this very thing, that He who began a good work in you will perfect it until the day of Christ Jesus.

The next four-weeks will move quickly. Life is short, eternity is forever. As you take deliberate steps toward deepening and developing your relationship with Jesus, my prayer and hope is that you see results beyond what you could ask or even imagine!

Step 3| Prepare

The four weeks in the workbook correspond with the four chapters in the book, One Simple Word (OSW). Be sure to read OSW before beginning. You can visit littorch.com to purchase an e-book or hard copy for yourself and / or partner.

Get ready to experience, explore and engage in the three ways questions are asked in the Bible. There are questions God asks you, questions you ask God and questions you ask others.

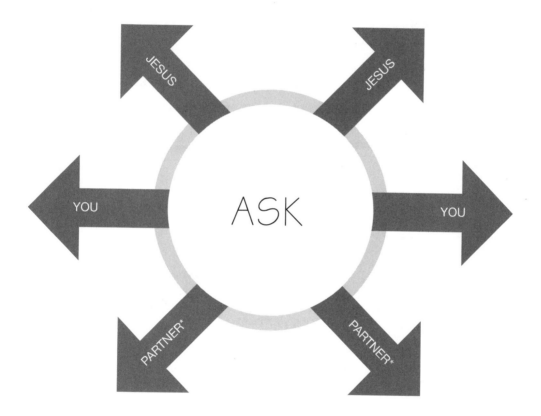

The format and flow of the workbook will be as follows:

MONDAYS| Jesus asks You

TUESDAYS| You ask Jesus

WEDNESDAYS| You ask your Partner* or Other

THURSDAYS| You ask You

FRIDAYS, SATURDAYS or SUNDAYS| Meet with your Partner/Group to discuss summary questions

Each of the four weeks contains three days of personal study (M, T, T) with two days of partner discussion questions (W and F). You will need about 15-20 minutes each day to complete your personal study. On Wednesdays, you may connect with your partner, preferably in person or at least by phone or email. And at the end of the week or on the weekend, it is important to meet in person to discuss the summary questions from Friday.

Preparation Checklist:

__ I have at least 15-20 minutes each morning for personal study over the next four weeks.

__ I have a copy of OSW, the OSWW and a Bible.

__ I have asked my partner to join me. My partner is:

__ I have at least 30 minutes each weekend to meet with my partner.

__ On Wednesdays, we will connect: in person / phone / or email (circle one).

__ On the weekend, choose a convenient place and time to meet for the next four-weeks.

_____ (signed / your name) _____ (date)

Step 4| Begin

You may be asking, "When is the best time to begin this study?" My suggestion is to begin on the Monday of the upcoming week. Don't wait. The time will never be just right. There will always be difficulty planning and coming up with reasons when other times will work best. Begin now and enjoy the benefits of interacting with God, His word and your partner. Throughout this study:

Ask Jesus for wisdom. Wisdom from above is different than the wisdom of this world. Your life will begin to look different as you become wise in the eyes of God. You'll experience a deeper relationship, a newfound trust and sweet dependence on Jesus as you look to Him for guidance and direction.

> **Philippians 1:9 (NIV)** And this is my prayer: that your love may abound more and more in knowledge and depth of insight.

Ask Jesus to teach you new things about Him. The Apostle Paul writes, "My purpose is that they may be encouraged in heart and united in love, so that they may have the full riches of complete understanding, in order that they may know the mystery of God, namely, Christ, in whom are hidden all the treasures of wisdom and knowledge. I tell you this so that no one may deceive you by fine-sounding arguments" **(Colossians 2:2-4)**.

> **Psalm 25:4 (NIV)** Show me your ways, O LORD, teach me your paths.

> **John 13:13 (NASB)** You call Me Teacher and Lord; and you are right, for so I am.

Ask Jesus to teach you new things about yourself.

> **Psalm 143:10 (NASB)** Teach me to do Your will, For You are my God; Let Your good Spirit lead me on level ground.

> **Psalm 139:23-24 (NIV)** Search me, O God, and know my heart; test me and know my anxious thoughts. See if there is any offensive way in me, and lead me in the way everlasting.

And ask that these next four weeks help deepen and develop many of the relationships in your life; first with the Lord and second with others.

One final thought, the questions we ask and the questions we answer can profoundly impact our lives. You may be tempted to give answers you think someone wants to hear. I would suggest not doing that. Be real, be transparent, seek to recognize what is really in your heart. Proverbs 27:9 says a man's earnest counsel is sweet to his friend.

Be a biblical friend. Be authentic with God and with your partner. This will help you grow immensely. The Bible says, "An honest answer is like a kiss on the lips" (Proverbs 24:26). Strive for honesty and authenticity in all your answers from the many questions ahead.

Enjoy this journey. Learn from the daily exercises. Be confident knowing there are great and precious promises in the Bible that you are about to experience (2 Peter 1:4).

As you progress through this study, you will see how magnificent Jesus is as the master conversationalist and also see how much delight and difficulty there is in becoming like Him.

Mark 10:36 NIV "What do you want me to do for you?" he asked.

Theme word: **SERVE**

WEEK ONE

JESUS' MOST FREQUENTLY ASKED QUESTION

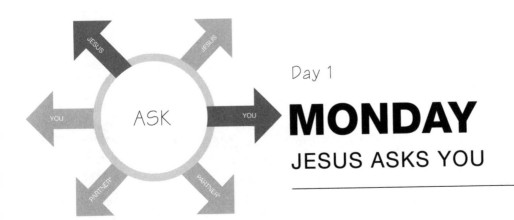

Day 1

MONDAY

JESUS ASKS YOU

What did you learn from reading chapter one, Jesus' Most Frequently Asked Question in OSW that was interesting or insightful?

In 2008, approximately 240 million calls were made to 911 to seek help for a police, fire or medical emergency. That is roughly 75% of America's population calling out for help.

In 1965, John Lennon from The Beatles wrote a song titled Help. The lyrics are:

> Help! I need somebody.
> Help! Not just anybody.
> Help! You know I need someone.
> Help! Won't you please, please help me?

People across the nation are calling out for help. John Lennon needed help. He asked for help, sang about help, and looked for it everywhere. The truth is that we all need help.[4]

How about you, when was the last time you asked for help? Were you glad you asked?

Have you ever considered where the Bible directs us to ask for help? Y / N

Write out Psalm 121:1-2.

Read Psalm 124:8. Where does our help come from?

Who do you normally turn to first when you need help?

Our help really comes from the Lord in all things. It can be a new thought to consider God as the source of all help and as the first person we should go to.

The saying "God helps those who help themselves" is not found in the Bible. The Bible actually teaches the opposite. It is those who realize they cannot help themselves who receive the most help from the Lord. There is only one place in the Bible that refers to those who help themselves. It is found in John 12:6. This passage refers to Judas as a thief and "used to help himself" to the money that was put into the money bag (NIV translation only).

> **John 12:6 (NIV)** He did not say this because he cared about the poor but because he was a thief; as keeper of the money bag, he used to help himself to what was put into it.

Now, let's focus on Jesus. Jesus is the greatest helper the world has ever seen and His most frequently asked question reveals this. Jesus frequently asks, **"What do you want Me to do for you?"** (Matthew 20:32, March 10:36, 10:51, Luke 18:41). Lives can be forever changed after answering Jesus' questions. He is the greatest source of help we could turn to.

Take some time and answer Jesus' most frequently asked question as if He were directly asking you, **"What do you want Me to do for you?"** Go ahead and just be still for a few moments. Answer Jesus' question as if He were sitting with you, listening and waiting for your response. Write your answers below.

Personally?

Professionally?

Spiritually?

SUGGESTION
Take at least 2-5 minutes and enjoy discussing Jesus' most frequently asked question with Him. The application for today really comes by having this conversation with Jesus.

Day one is complete. You are on your way and about to enjoy many conversations with Jesus and with others about Jesus. You just had a conversation with Him and answered one of His questions. Well done. There are questions Jesus asks us, questions we ask Jesus and questions we ask others. Tomorrow is your turn to ask Him a question.

Day 1

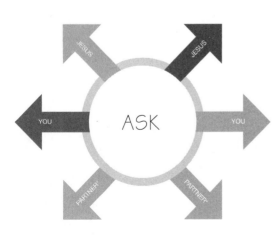

Day 2

TUESDAY
YOU ASK JESUS

Jesus is all knowing. He is God. He knows you best. He even knows what you need before you ask. However, He still asks that we ask.

Read Matthew 6:8. What does Jesus say your Heavenly Father knows?

Write out Ephesians 3:20

What is God able to do according to this verse?

In both passages above, it may seem obvious but we are instructed to _____ God for what we need (hint: this is one simple word with three letters).

What do you think prevents most people from asking God for help?

What prevents you?

Strong independence, lack of knowledge, pride, stubbornness or even fear can prevent us from asking. Sometimes we are scared to ask God for help. It's not that we don't believe He can help us, we may fear He will in a way we didn't expect.

Various reasons come up for not asking for help. We may think we don't even need help. Or, asking for help belittles us. Yet, humility is the antidote. Christian author C.S. Lewis wrote, "If anyone would like to acquire humility, I can, I think, tell him the first step. The first step is to realize that one is proud. And a biggish step, too. At least, nothing whatever can be done before it. If you think you are not conceited, it means you are very conceited indeed."[5]

Read a few of these examples and see if you are proud or humble:

- Proud people feel confident in how much they know.
- Humble people are aware of how very much they have to learn.

- Proud people are defensive when criticized.
- Humble people receive criticism with a gentle, open spirit.

- Proud people have a hard time saying, "I was wrong. Will you please forgive me?"
- Humble people are quick to admit their failure, and to seek forgiveness when necessary.

- Proud people compare themselves with others, and feel worthy of honor.
- Humble people compare themselves with the holiness of God and feel a desperate need for His mercy.

- Proud people desire to be served.
- Humble people are motivated to serve others.

Did you relate to any of the proud descriptions above? The Apostle Paul writes, "For by the grace given me I say to every one of you: Do not think of yourself more highly than you ought, but rather think of yourself with sober judgment, in accordance with the measure of faith God has given you" (Romans 12:3). Circle the statements from the list that seemed to apply to you. Most of us need help fighting against pride, we just don't realize it.

The one thing that God is opposed to 100% of the time throughout the Bible, is pride. James 4:6 says, "God is opposed to the proud but gives grace to the humble." The proud never ask God for help. The proud don't even see their need for help. Meanwhile, the humble receive grace from Jesus because they come to Him knowing they need help in all things and repeatedly ask for God's help.

> **1 Peter 5:5-6 (NIV)** All of you, clothe yourselves with humility toward one another, because, "God opposes the proud but gives grace to the humble." Humble yourselves, therefore, under God's mighty hand, that he may lift you up in due time.

> **Proverbs 16:5 (NIV)** The LORD detests all the proud of heart. Be sure of this: They will not go unpunished.

> **Proverbs 21:4 (NIV)** Haughty eyes and a proud heart, the lamp of the wicked, are sin!

Take a moment and write out the three things God gives to all people from Acts 17:25.

1 |

2 |

3 |

Day 2

Sometimes our pride will have us forget that everything is from God: life, breath, everything.

> **James 1:16-18 (NIV)** Don't be deceived, my dear brothers. Every good and perfect gift is from above, coming down from the Father of the heavenly lights, who does not change like shifting shadows. He chose to give us birth through the word of truth that we might be a kind of first fruits of all he created.

God gives us everything and He can help us with anything. We know this. With this in mind, what should we be asking for: Cars? Clothes? Cash? Sometimes He does give us these things; at other times, He does not. However, a close personal relationship with Him is what we need most now and for eternity. Perhaps, this is what we should be asking for?

How about asking Jesus for help in developing a close, personal relationship with Him in the days ahead?

Write the out James 4:8. If you come near to God, what will He do?

Read Psalm 103:1-2. What do you see as the benefits from a relationship with God?

After answering the question above, read through Psalm 103:3-22 and list a few of the biblical benefits that come from a relationship with the Lord.

SUGGESTION
Contact your partner via phone, email or text and schedule a time to connect to answer tomorrow's partner questions. I would strongly suggest meeting in person, if possible, or at least by phone call. This exercise should take about 10-15 minutes.

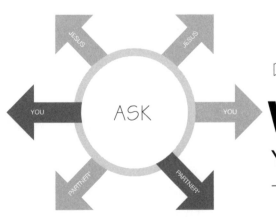

Day 3

WEDNESDAY
YOU ASK PARTNER

TODAY IS A DAY FOR YOU TO ASK YOUR PARTNER A FEW QUESTIONS.

You can discover so much about a person if you ask them questions and listen attentively. The right question can open the doorway to a person's heart as Jesus said, "For out of the overflow of the heart the mouth speaks" (Matthew 12:34). Asking the right question at the right time is a skill. And to say the right words at the right time is an art for "a man has joy in an apt answer and how delightful is a timely word" (Proverbs 15:23). The time to start developing this skill and art is now.

Three questions to ask your partner today are below. Relax and enjoy the conversation. Take a deep breath. Don't try to impress one another with your answers. Be genuine. Be sincere and share whatever comes to mind when responding.

You will be asked these same questions. Look to honor one another by sincerely and diligently serving and fulfilling the request within the boundaries of Scripture. Our desire to consider others above our own desires is not natural. This is supernatural. It is above the natural. The more we consider the needs of others above our own, the more we become like Christ.

> **Philippians 2:4-7 (NIV)** says, "Each of you should look not only to your own interests, but also to the interests of others. Your attitude should be the same as that of Christ Jesus: Who, being in very nature God, did not consider equality with God something to be grasped, but made himself nothing, taking the very nature of a servant, being made in human likeness."

PARTNER DISCUSSION:

1. Over the last several weeks, what is a thoughtful thing someone has done for you?

Your answer:

Partner's answer:

2. Over the last several weeks, what is a thoughtful thing you have done for someone else?

Your answer:

Partner's answer:

3. What would you like me to do for you?

Your answer:

Partner's answer:

⊕ SUGGESTION
Share something specific that your partner could do for you in
the upcoming week.

Don't ask your partner for something far-fetched like building you a rocket ship to the moon. While they probably could do that, ask them to do something to be completed over the next few days. And if you are asking them to pray for you, be specific with who, what, when and how you would like the prayer focused.

Have fun living out the golden rule today which says, "In everything, therefore, treat people the same way you want them to treat you, for this is the Law and the Prophets" (Matthew 7:12).

Also, Jesus asked for help many times throughout Scripture. He asked a Samaritan woman for a drink.

> **John 4:7-9 (NIV)** When a Samaritan woman came to draw water, Jesus said to her, "Will you give me a drink?" (His disciples had gone into the town to buy food.) The Samaritan woman said to him, "You are a Jew and I am a Samaritan woman. How can you ask me for a drink?" (For Jews do not associate with Samaritans.)

He asked His disciples to bring Him a donkey.

> **Mark 11:1-4 (NIV)** As they approached Jerusalem and came to Bethphage and Bethany at the Mount of Olives, Jesus sent two of his disciples, saying to them, "Go to the village ahead of you, and just as you enter it, you will find a colt tied there, which no one has ever ridden. Untie it and bring it here. If anyone asks you, 'Why are you doing this?' tell him, 'The Lord needs it and will send it back here shortly.'"

God can do anything. He is the Creator and we are the created. When Jesus asks for help, He is inviting people into a relationship. Jesus cared about His disciples by giving them the opportunity to do something for Him. As you ask your partner for help, you are inviting them into your life.

One last thing, synch with your partner and agree upon a time and place for your meeting this weekend to discuss Friday's summary questions. A comfortable environment would be best.

Day 3

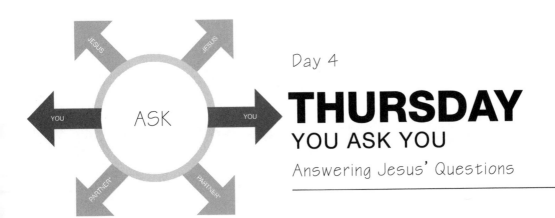

Day 4

THURSDAY
YOU ASK YOU
Answering Jesus' Questions

Jesus gave us the perfect example to study and follow. Even as a young child He was in the temple courts "sitting among the teachers, listening and asking them questions" (Luke 2:46). As you pattern your life by obeying Jesus, you will find yourself growing in wisdom and in favor with God and among others (Luke 2:52).

In John 13:13 Jesus says to His disciples, "You call Me Teacher and Lord; and you are right, for so I am." Jesus is continually teaching and over the last few days, you have been learning a lot from Him. Jesus has asked you questions, you have asked Him questions and you have also asked your partner questions.

Today, I want to help you draw near to God and answer a few of Jesus' questions from the Gospels. Questions can be like a barometer in a relationship. They can start general and cool and then move into very personal and hot topics.

Answer these questions as if Jesus were speaking with you. Read the Scriptures below and write your response afterwards. Many great teachers ask simple questions to draw out from the students what the teacher already knows. Jesus knows your answer to these questions, but do you?

BE HONEST. BE AUTHENTIC. BE REAL AND BE CLEAR WITH GOD AS YOU ANSWER HIS QUESTIONS.

What are you seeking? (John 1:38)

Why are you seeking Me? (Luke 2:49)

Who do you say I am? (Matthew 16:15)

Personal relationships grow by being honest and clear when asked a question. God knows our answers even before we do and yet He still asks timeless questions to bring us into a relationship to learn more about Him and to recognize who He is.

In Luke 12:24-26, Jesus says, "Consider the ravens: They do not sow or reap, they have no storeroom or barn; yet God feeds them. And how much more valuable you are than birds! Who of you by worrying can add a single hour to his life? Since you cannot do this very little thing, why do you worry about the rest?"

If Jesus were to ask you, why do you worry? How would you respond? Take a few moments and write out your worries.

The Apostle Paul writes in Philippians 4:6 to make your "requests known to God." Asking allows us to seek the Lord for help, even with our worries. From the worries you have listed, present your worries and requests to the Lord and make them known by asking for help. Just close your eyes and have this conversation with Jesus.

___ I have made these requests known to God through prayer and will wait patiently for His response.
___ I believe the Lord may have me wait for His timing. While this is difficult, I ask for His help not to worry.

> **Psalm 5:3 (NIV)** In the morning, O LORD, you hear my voice; in the morning I lay my requests before you and wait in expectation.

> **Psalm 130:5 (NASB)** I wait for the LORD, my soul does wait, And in His word do I hope.

Jesus asks, "Who of you by worrying can add a single hour to his life?" He then gives us clear instruction to "seek first His kingdom and His righteousness, and all these things (food, clothing, shelter) will be added to you. 'So do not worry about tomorrow; for tomorrow will care for itself. Each day has enough trouble of its own'" (Matthew 6:33-34).

Life can be filled with worries; however, when we know the care and compassion of our Heavenly Father, we are reminded that He will provide us what we need, not necessarily what we want, but most certainly what we need as we seek Him first.

> **Romans 8:31-32 (NIV)** What, then, shall we say in response to this? If God is for us, who can be against us? He who did not spare his own Son, but gave him up for us all--how will he not also, along with him, graciously give us all things?

> **Matthew 6:33 (NIV)** But seek first his kingdom and his righteousness, and all these things will be given to you as well.

As you grow in your relationship with Jesus, conversations with Him and about Him will increase. The Creator of the universe knows your worries and He knows yours needs. You will be comforted amid your worries and concerns knowing God never gives us more than we can handle. He is continually working all things together for our good. Even when we don't know how this could be possible, Jesus invites us to come to Him.

> **Matthew 11:28-29 (NASB)** Come to Me, all who are weary and heavy-laden, and I will give you rest. Take My yoke upon you and learn from Me, for I am gentle and humble in heart, and YOU WILL FIND REST FOR YOUR SOULS.

Day 4

SUGGESTION
Take a prayer walk. Simply go outside and walk around your home, the block, park, office, school, wherever. Literally talk with God about His questions and your answers from today.

This can be an intimate and important conversation that will deepen and develop your relationship with the Lord Jesus Christ. Also, present your worries to Him. Ask for His help and guidance with all your concerns. Your Heavenly Father knows what you need even before you ask; however, He still asks that we ask (Matthew 6:8) and is pleased when His children come to Him for help.

Day 5

FRIDAY

SUMMARY & REFLECTION

As a reminder, this workbook was designed to help you do two things:

1 | Talk with Jesus
2 | Talk with others about Jesus using one simple word.

Deuteronomy 6:5-9 (NIV) Love the LORD your God with all your heart and with all your soul and with all your strength. These commandments that I give you today are to be upon your hearts. Impress them on your children. Talk about them when you sit at home and when you walk along the road, when you lie down and when you get up. Tie them as symbols on your hands and bind them on your foreheads. Write them on the doorframes of your houses and on your gates.

As you talk with God and talk with others about God, you will find your relationships coming alive. The right use of questions will enhance many of your relationships. Using questions with the goal to listen and learn will change you. This change will allow your relationships to deepen and develop, not only with God but with others as well. The wrong use of questions will distance and discourage conversation if the questions are used to interrogate instead of genuine inquiry.

For today's exercise, carefully consider the questions. Search your heart and give specific answers that are really yours, not what you think you are supposed to say. Others will appreciate your authenticity and be encouraged by the personal details of how God is building your relationships with Him through your commitment to this study. Some questions can be answered light-heartedly and others can be discussed deeply if you like.

Your answers from today will be discussed with your partner at your agreed upon time this weekend. Prepare your answers prior to meeting. Answer all of the personal questions and choose at least two of the group questions to discuss. Your partner will also choose at least two questions. Consider sharing a few of your answers from your personal section as well if times allows.

PERSONAL QUESTIONS:

1. What is your most frequently asked question? What makes you ask this question so often?

2. What did you come into this study expecting? What has surprised you?

3. As you reflect over the last week, what were some helpful concepts, ideas or questions you learned from this chapter?

4. With whom do you have the best conversations about God? How come?

PARTNER DISCUSSION QUESTIONS (circle at least two):

1. How would your life change if your most frequently asked question became: What would you like me to do for you?

2. What one piece of knowledge will you begin using in your personal, professional or spiritual life? Give an example of how you will apply this and when you will begin.

3. While doing this study, what opportunities have you had to talk with others about Jesus?

4. What personal question from the previous section would you like to ask your partner?

One week down, three more to go. Seeing Jesus as the Master communicator and embracing His most frequently asked question could change your life. What if you were to begin more personal, professional and even spiritual conversations with, "What is one thing you would like me to do for you today?"

CONGRATULATIONS, 23 DAYS TO GO!

Next week, you will explore the first question ever asked or as I like to call it, the greatest trick in the book. Have a restful weekend and consider rereading chapter two from One Simple Word to prepare for the week ahead.

Day 5

Genesis 3:1 (NIV) Now the serpent was more crafty than any of the wild animals the LORD God had made. He said to the woman, "Did God really say, 'You must not eat from any tree in the garden'?"

Theme word: **AWARE**

WEEKTWO
FIRST QUESTION EVER ASKED

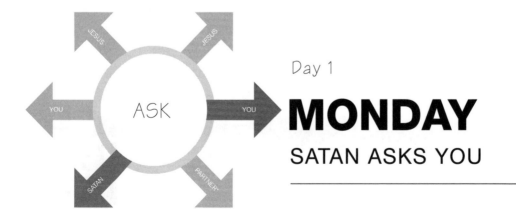

Day 1

MONDAY

SATAN ASKS YOU

Have you ever considered that Satan wants to have a relationship with you? Y / N

What do you think is Satan's favorite tool, his favorite technique, and most effective trick to bring you into a relationship with him? What is your guess?

Would it surprise you that this is the same tool and technique Jesus uses? Deviously and defiantly, Satan looks to deceive you through a question. Satan wants you to listen to him and he uses questions to direct the conversation toward doubting what God has said. I would say this is the greatest trick in the book and it is probably the number one trick he still uses today.

Do not be <u>deceived</u>, Satan has an agenda with specific goals he would like to see happen in this relationship. Read John 10:10 and list the three things the thief (Satan) wants to do in your life:

1|

2|

3|

Jesus also invites you to have a relationship with Him. From John 10:10, what type of life does Jesus offer you?

The Bible is our instruction book for relationships, communication and how to obey the Lord who guides us in paths of righteousness for His name's sake (Psalm 23:3). Satan wants you to listen to his voice, rather than God's. And his path will begin with pleasure but leave you in pain. Sadly, many of us fall prey to this trick time and time again.

Write out the first question ever asked in Genesis 3:1. This is the first question ever recorded in all of history.

What is Satan (the serpent) questioning?

Knowing what the Scripture says will aid you in your battle against Satan. As Jesus was tempted by the devil in the desert He continually responded with, "It is written . . . It is written . . . It is written . . ." (Matthew 4:4-11) Jesus Christ gave us His example to follow. Satan knows the Scriptures extraordinarily well. That is why for us, knowing God's Word is imperative to fight spiritual battle so that we "can encourage others by sound doctrine and refute those who oppose it" (Titus 1:9).

Read 2 Corinthians 11:3. What was the Apostle Paul afraid would happen to our minds? Circle the answer below.

> **2 Corinthians 11:3 (NASB)** But I am afraid that, as the serpent deceived Eve by his craftiness, your minds will be led astray from the simplicity and purity of devotion to Christ.

In what area(s) has Satan been leading you astray from the simplicity and purity of devotion to the Lord?

What promise(s) of God is Satan twisting and getting you to doubt?

The greatest strategy for defeating Satan is found in the same way Jesus did it, by knowing and responding with God's Word.

> **2 Corinthians 10:4-5 (NIV)** The weapons we fight with are not the weapons of the world. On the contrary, they have divine power to demolish strongholds. We demolish arguments and every pretension that sets itself up against the knowledge of God, and we take captive every thought to make it obedient to Christ.

> **Ephesians 6:17 (NIV)** Take the helmet of salvation and the sword of the Spirit, which is the word of God.

> **Philippians 4:6-7 (NIV)** Do not be anxious about anything, but in everything, by prayer and petition, with thanksgiving, present your requests to God. And the peace of God, which transcends all understanding, will guard your hearts and your minds in Christ Jesus.

We must learn to listen and acknowledge what God has said. Write out John 10:27.

Whose voice are we to hear and whose voice are we to follow?

Knowing Jesus' voice by knowing His words allows us to recognize the lies Satan spins. Satan will ask you to doubt what God has said. Jesus continually responds by saying, "It is written . . it is written . . ."

Day 1

As you become more familiar with the Bible, when someone asks, "Did God really say?" quickly search the Scriptures to find an answer instead of responding with, "I feel . . ." or "I'm not sure . . ." or "I don't know. . ." If you respond with your own thoughts, feelings and words—you risk being deceived and led astray. Satan will have you right where he wants you—listening to his voice and engaged in a conversation with him.

Keep in mind that throughout the Gospels, the Pharisees knew the Scriptures very well and quoted many passages; however, they were unable to recognize Jesus as the living word and Spirit. Jesus spoke directly to them when He said:

> **John 6:63 (NIV)** The Spirit gives life; the flesh counts for nothing. The words I have spoken to you are spirit and they are life.

The Holy Spirit gives life and it is not enough to know Scripture. We have to live in dependence on God's Spirit to guide, lead and direct us. As Jesus said:

> **John 16:13 (NASB)** But when He, the Spirit of truth, comes, He will guide you into all the truth.

Continually ask God to guide you through the Scriptures and here are a few suggestions to help you remember what God has said. Choose at least one to do today.

> 1| Go for a walk. Talk with God. Schedule time for prayer. Think about what is capturing your attention. What things, people or distractions are keeping your focus away from being obedient to God? Ask the Lord to show you the distractions Satan is using in your life. Make a list and attach appropriate Bible passages that will help you implement godly changes.

> 2| Take an inventory of who you associate with. Who is influencing your life the most at this moment? Scripture says, "He who walks with the wise grows wise, but a companion of fools suffers harm" (Proverbs 13:20). 1 Corinthians 15:33 reminds us, "Do not be misled: Bad company corrupts good character." James 3:13 asks, "Who is wise and understanding among you? Let him show it by his good life, by deeds done in the humility that comes from wisdom." Ask God to bring wise people into your life and seek them out as well.

> 3| Schedule a specific time to meet with God on your calendar. During that time, read your Bible and listen to God speak to you through the Scriptures. Begin keeping a prayer journal and write down your prayer requests (Philippians 4:6). Make this a daily habit. Cherish and look forward to this time each day as you grow in the "grace and knowledge of the Lord" (2 Peter 3:18).

Which number(s) did you select to do today?   1 / 2 / 3

⊕ SUGGESTION
Memorize John 10:10. Share this with your partner on the weekend. Keep conversing with Jesus by listening to His voice and His words as He speaks to you through the Bible.

This week's theme word is "aware." The exercises above are suggested to help you become more aware of the questions you are being asked and the questions you are answering. Remind yourself that Satan wants to have a relationship with you and part of that relationship involves leading your mind astray from the simplicity and purity of devotion to the Lord.

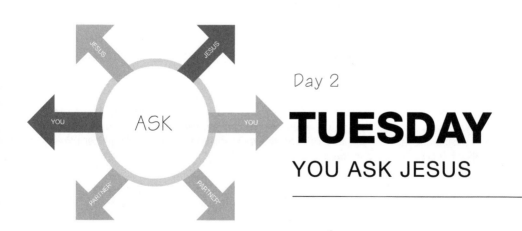

Day 2

TUESDAY
YOU ASK JESUS

Movies, cartoons and television portray Satan much differently than how the Bible describes him. How do cartoons and most movies portray Satan? Does a specific scene or image come to mind?

LET'S LOOK AT HOW THE BIBLE PORTRAYS SATAN.

As you read Genesis 3:1, Satan is described as more _____ than any other created beast that the Lord God has made. What do you think is the reason God is telling us that Satan is more crafty than any other created being?

Read 2 Corinthians 11:14-15. How does Satan disguise himself? How different is this than how the world describes Satan?

> **2 Corinthians 11:14-15 (NASB)** No wonder, for even Satan disguises himself as an angel of light. Therefore it is not surprising if his servants also disguise themselves as servants of righteousness, whose end will be according to their deeds.

Write out 2 Corinthians 2:11, what does the Bible say we are not to be ignorant or unaware of?

On a scale of 1 to 10 with 10 being the most aware, how aware are you of Satan's schemes?

| 1 | 2 | 3 | 4 | 5 | 6 | 7 | 8 | 9 | 10 |

On a scale of 1 to 10 with 10 being the most aware, how do you think your partner will rate you?

| 1 | 2 | 3 | 4 | 5 | 6 | 7 | 8 | 9 | 10 |

On a scale of 1 to 10 with 10 being the most aware, how aware would you rate your partner?

| 1 | 2 | 3 | 4 | 5 | 6 | 7 | 8 | 9 | 10 |

God's second question to Adam was, "Who told you that you were naked?" (Gen 3:11) In other words, who have you been listening to? We need to learn to be continually aware of who we are listening to and the questions they are asking.

Satan lies all the time and one of his biggest lies is pretending to know the future. Only God knows the future. But cunningly, Satan will try to trick you into doubting God's desire to meet your needs. God's word declares that everything you need will be given in His timeframe, not necessarily yours. Satan wants you to doubt this by acting impulsively instead of patiently waiting for the Lord's response. Read and consider these passages.

Isaiah 40:31 (NASB) Yet those who wait for the LORD Will gain new strength; They will mount up with wings like eagles, They will run and not get tired, They will walk and not become weary.

Psalm 84:11-12 (NIV) For the LORD God is a sun and shield; the LORD bestows favor and honor; no good thing does he withhold from those whose walk is blameless. O LORD Almighty, blessed is the man who trusts in you.

Philippians 4:19 (NIV) And my God will meet all your needs according to his glorious riches in Christ Jesus.

Choose one of the passages above and read it aloud a few times. Really, take time to do this. You will find it comforting as you are made aware of these promises. Do your best to bring one of the verses into a conversation today whether at home, school or work. Many times we don't like waiting and we do forget what God has said. Completing this exercise can remind you to speak the words of God to yourself and to others.

Remember who you are dealing with. Satan is not only out to hurt you, he wants to utterly destroy you. Begin thinking about the greatest battles in your life right now. Are they in your marriage? In your thoughts? With family? Friends? Finances? Past relationships? Drugs? Alcohol?

Ask God to show you more of the distractions Satan is using in your life that keep interrupting you from studying your Bible, praying and having fellowship with other believers. List a few that come to mind.

1|

2|

3|

Here are a few passages to encourage you to keep meeting with your partner over the next few weeks.

Hebrews 10:24-25 (NIV) And let us consider how we may spur one another on toward love and good deeds. Let us not give up meeting together, as some are in the habit of doing, but let us encourage one another--and all the more as you see the Day approaching.

Hebrews 3:12-14 (NIV) See to it, brothers, that none of you has a sinful, unbelieving heart that turns away from the living God. But encourage one another daily, as long as it is called Today, so that none of you may be hardened by sin's deceitfulness. We have come to share in Christ if we hold firmly till the end the confidence we had at first.

In your own words, what do you think is the importance of meeting face to face instead of via phone or electronically?

Day 2

Write at least one reason Satan may not want you meeting in person with your partner. Look up Proverbs 20:18 and 24:6, 2 John 12 after writing your answer.

Tomorrow, you will become more aware of the distractions Satan is using and will then develop a plan to help combat these distractions. Continue taking time to reflect and pray over the Scriptures that are provided.

Satan hates it when Christians come together to discuss the words of God. While Satan wants to prevent this, Jesus encourages this and loves it when His children seek Him and discuss His words. Keep seeking first God's kingdom (Matthew 6:33) and you will be surprised at the rewards God has waiting for you (Hebrews 11:6).

AS YOUR RELATIONSHIP WITH JESUS GROWS, BE REMINDED THAT:

Psalm 46:1-2 (NIV) God is our refuge and strength, an ever-present help in trouble. Therefore we will not fear.

1 Corinthians 15:57 (NIV) But thanks be to God! He gives us the victory through our Lord Jesus Christ.

SUGGESTION
Suggestion: Continue to ask God to reveal areas of "distractions" in your life. Remember, Satan wants to get you isolated while God wants you to come together. Also, contact your partner to confirm tomorrow's meeting in person or by phone.

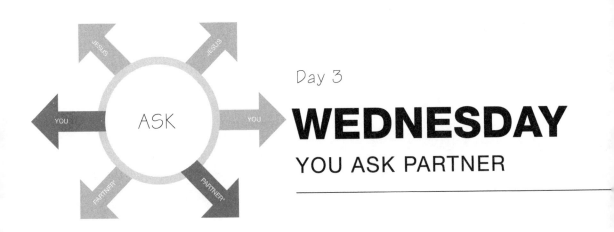

Day 3

WEDNESDAY

YOU ASK PARTNER

We are not to be unaware of Satan's schemes (2 Corinthians 2:11). By believing Satan's lies and disobeying God, we will suffer and there will be pain in our lives. We do not have to learn the hard way. We can learn the right way by listening to God.

Mother Teresa was a Roman Catholic nun who founded the Missionaries of Charity and won the Nobel Peace Prize for her humanitarian work. She was once asked, "In all your years of service to God, what do you think prevents most people from developing a rich spiritual life?" She responded very quickly and said, "That's easy. The answer can be captured in one word. Just one word. Distractions. Too many distractions."

We all have distractions in our lives that may be preventing us from developing a deeper and more intimate spiritual life with Jesus. Three of the top distractions Satan uses are found in the parable of the sower. Read Mark 4:19 and list the three things that choke the word of God from our lives.

1|

2|

3|

Does Satan continually distract or deceive you with any of these three things? Specifically, in what ways does he do this in your life?

Here are a few distractions in my life and how I battle against them.

Distraction| WORLDLINESS & MATERIALISM

New Focus / Scripture
Living with less while enjoying whatever God provides. Choosing people over possessions every time (1 John 2:15-17).

Action Steps
Each day give a kind word, possession or act of service to someone (2 Corinthians9:7). Striving for a minimalistic lifestyle.

Distraction| IDLE CONVERSATIONS

New Focus / Scripture
Engaging others with conversations about God and the Scriptures (Deuteronomy 6, Colossians 4:5-6, Ephesians 6:19-20).

Action Steps
Writing books about God and asking the questions God uses in the Bible with friends, family and people I meet.

Distraction | SELFISHNESS

New Focus / Scripture
Thinking about how to serve others. Godly thoughts and examples of servant-leadership (Philippians 2:3-4; 4:8, Matthew 6:33, Romans 12:1-2).

Action Steps
Asking, "How can I help?" Sharing resources, study tools and inviting others to Bible studies and prayer groups.

LIST THE WAYS YOU ARE DISTRACTED AND WRITE A NEW FOCUS AND ACTION STEP:

Distraction	New Focus / Scripture	Action Steps
Technology?		

Share your list with your partner. If any of the distractions on your partner's list apply to your life, add it to your list now. Discuss action steps and how you can specifically help your partner become more aware of the distractions in his / her life.

PARTNER DISCUSSION:

1. Over the last several weeks, which distraction on your list has prevented you the most from drawing closer to Jesus?

Your answer:

Partner's answer:

Day 3

2. Over the next several weeks, what specifically will you do to correct this?

Your answer:

Partner's answer:

3. Ask your partner, what would you like me to do for you this week?

Your answer:

Partner's answer:

SUGGESTION
Pray specifically for the Lord to reveal any other distractions
that are occurring in your life.

Asking for help and receiving help from others can be more difficult than we realize. Many of us have become quite independent and would rather be seen as self-sufficient. We really do not like asking others for help thinking it is inconvenient, unnecessary or just a burden for another. While this may be true, Jesus said it is more blessed to give than to receive (Acts 20:35). The more we learn to give help through prayers and acts of service, the more we become like Christ.

This week, be sure to help your partner with whatever request they have. Biblical community and friendship will grow as you apply God's word from 1 John 4:7, "Dear friends, let us love one another, for love comes from God. Everyone who loves has been born of God and knows God."

You both are doing great. Continue to be intentional about meeting with God and one another and confirm your meeting time and venue for this weekend. Your best days are yet ahead . . .

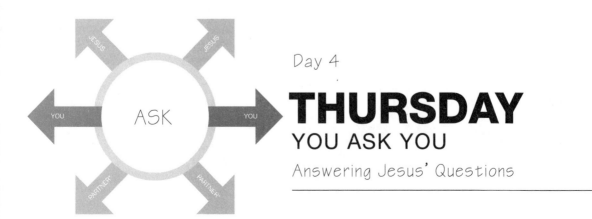

Day 4

THURSDAY
YOU ASK YOU
Answering Jesus' Questions

Satan will ask you questions. His continuous and subtle strategy is to get you doubting what God has said. The first question ever asked is one of the greatest tricks in the book.

The more we have conversations about God's Word and remind one another about what God has said, the more we will be spared the pain and sorrow that comes from being impacted by Satan's schemes. As you learned earlier this week, 2 Corinthians 2:11 specifically warns us not to be unaware of his tactics. By now, you are probably more aware of the schemes he has been using in your life.

Another one of Satan's favorite schemes is to have you isolated and separated from God and other believers. This is not a good place to be.

> **Proverbs 18:1 (NASB)** He who separates himself seeks his own desire, He quarrels against all sound wisdom.

> **Proverbs 14:12 (NIV)** There is a way that seems right to a man, but in the end it leads to death.

God wants to bring His family together. It is a blessing from God to have other believers helping you follow His words and teaching you to obey His commands. We must train ourselves to listen to the voice of the Lord and to trust His Words. Knowing God's voice steers us clear of Satan's tricks and we know God's voice by knowing the Scriptures.

Ask yourself, how well do you know the Scriptures? On a scale of 1 to 10 with 10 being very knowledgeable, how would you rate your knowledge of the Scriptures?

1   2   3   4   5   6   7   8   9   10

If you rated yourself low, thank you for being honest. That could mean there is a lot of room for growth and we all start out not knowing our Bibles very well. If you rated yourself high, you could be a great help to those who are just beginning in their Bible study. But, whether you consider yourself highly knowledgeable or just starting out, never neglect the necessity of study and growing in your dependence of God's Spirit to guide your thinking. By going through this workbook, you are headed in the right direction to know, follow and discuss what "is written". It is very important to continually focus on Jesus and the instruction from the Bible.

Jesus is the model of the greatest helper and the greatest servant the world has and will ever see. He came "not to be served but to serve" (Matt 20:28, Mark 10:45) and His life was focused on doing exactly what His Father asked Him to do. The closeness of Jesus' relationship with His Father centered around love and always doing what the Father asked.

Write out John 14:31 (NIV or NAS). How did Jesus show His love to the Father and to the whole world?

How would your life change if you did exactly what God asked you to do?

Read 1 John 5:2-4. What is God asking you to do?

1 John 5:2-4 (NASB) By this we know that we love the children of God, when we love God and observe His commandments. For this is the love of God, that we keep His commandments; and His commandments are not burdensome. For whatever is born of God overcomes the world; and this is the victory that has overcome the world—our faith.

Is there a specific command(s) that comes to mind that God is asking you to obey? Which command will you choose to show your love for God by obeying Him today? Write it below.

Do not be deceived, a fulfilling life awaits you as you do what Jesus asks. Satan's invitations and requests are a lie and will leave you unsatisfied and disappointed every time. It is a privilege to do what God has commanded. The commands of God were written for our good.

Deuteronomy 10:12-13 (NIV) And now, O Israel, what does the LORD your God ask of you but to fear the LORD your God, to walk in all his ways, to love him, to serve the LORD your God with all your heart and with all your soul, and to observe the LORD's commands and decrees that I am giving you today for your own good?

SUGGESTION
Express your love for God today by obeying at least one of the
commands you wrote above.

As your love for Jesus grows, your desire to obey Him will flow from that love. Asking Jesus questions and responding to His questions is a primary way of developing this relationship. Obedience becomes a by-product of this relationship and your desire to please Him will be the result. This was the example modeled for us as Jesus knew the Father's love and always did the things that were pleasing to Him.

Day 4

John 8:29 (NASB) And He who sent Me is with Me; He has not left Me alone, for I always do the things that are pleasing to Him.

May we follow Jesus' example and make this our ambition as well, to be pleasing to God. The Apostle Paul set this as his goal and encourages us to do the same.

2 Corinthians 5:9 (NIV) So we make it our goal to please him, whether we are at home in the body or away from it.

Our perfect example is Jesus. As we express our love for the Lord may we learn to joyfully obey His commands and turn away from Satan's distractions. As Jesus said, "If you love Me, you will keep My commandments" (John 14:15). Keeping God's commands is a way to express love to Him. And now may we ask and encourage one another to do this as well, to live a life pleasing to God.

1 Thessalonians 4:1 (NIV) Finally, brothers, we instructed you how to live in order to please God, as in fact you are living. Now we ask you and urge you in the Lord Jesus to do this more and more.

Day 5

FRIDAY

SUMMARY & REFLECTION

Always remember, the questions we ask and the questions we answer can profoundly impact our lives. Satan has a specific agenda with his questions. His desire is to steal, kill and destroy you (John 10:10). It is wise for us to become acutely aware of how Satan will use questions to establish a relationship in your life that will draw you away from God.

Over the years, I have asked many people, "Has there ever been a question that completely changed your life?" One 82-year old man recounted how 36 years ago he was asked, "Would you like to go to a meeting?" The meeting was Alcoholics Anonymous. His life changed after answering "yes" and has been sober ever since. For one 29-year-old in California the life-changing question was, "Do you wanna take a hit?" He regretted not saying, "No" and got caught up in a life of drugs.

Another person responded yes to, "Want to stay at this party and have one more drink?" This answer resulted in getting a DUI and ending up in jail. A young girl said yes to, "Would you like to come over and spend the night?" This resulted in an unexpected pregnancy.

Proverbs 1:10 says, "If sinners entice you, do not consent." It is wise to learn to say "no" to invitations or enticements that lead you away from obeying Christ.

> **Titus 2:11-13 (NIV)** For the grace of God that brings salvation has appeared to all men. It teaches us to say "No" to ungodliness and worldly passions, and to live self-controlled, upright and godly lives in this present age, while we wait for the blessed hope--the glorious appearing of our great God and Savior, Jesus Christ.

So much of our daily life rests in the decision of whether or not we will follow and obey Christ. It is a battle and a fight for our thoughts, attention and daily walk of obedience. This battle is not easy. However, the best decision we can make each day is to trust and obey the commands of God.

The last words we ever hear from Jesus's mother, Mary, are, "Do whatever He tells you" (John 2:5 NIV). Think about what your life would look like if:

1. You did everything Satan tells you to do. What would this be like for you?

2. You did everything Jesus tells you to do. What would this life look like for you?

Spend time today reflecting on your answers above. This week has personal and group discussion questions. I have also added an "extra" section for those who would like to go even deeper into this week's study.

PERSONAL DISCUSSION QUESTIONS:

1. What has God revealed to you about the distractions Satan is using in your life?

2. Read through 1 Thessalonians 2:17-20. Have there been attempts to prevent you from meeting with your partner? How beneficial has it been for you to meet face to face?

3. What is it that Satan may be asking you to do that you know you shouldn't be doing?

4. What do you sense Jesus is asking you to do that you just do not want to do? How come this may be so difficult?

PARTNER DISCUSSION QUESTIONS (choose at least two):

1. How would your life change if you responded to most questions with, "It is written . . . "?

2. Share one thing you learned from this chapter that you look forward to sharing with others.

3. How did you rate yourself on Tuesday and how would you rate yourself now in regard to being aware of Satan's schemes? Also, discuss how you rated your partner and how you can help one another become more aware of the distractions in your life.

Day 5

EXTRA DISCUSSION:

We say to err is human but to forgive is _____.[6] **When we experience forgiveness, we are experiencing the divine nature of God. When we extend forgiveness, we are being like God and sharing the grace, love and mercy God has extended toward us.**

1. What do you think is the reason God wants us to be aware of Satan's schemes?

2. Have you ever considered that the context of the passage from 2 Corinthians 2:11 deals with forgiveness? Y / N / I do now!

Read 2 Corinthians 2:7-10 to understand the passage in context.

3. Many people can recite what is commonly referred to as the Lord's Prayer found in Matthew 6:9-13. It begins with Our Father who is in heaven . . . Would you happen to know the verse immediately following this prayer in verse 14-15? Write it below.

4. Is there anyone in your life that you have not forgiven as Christ has forgiven you? What "scheme" may Satan be using in this relationship? Look up and meditate on Colossians 3:13 and Ephesians 4:32-5:1-2 for direction and what God may be asking you to do.

SUGGESTION
Before you go to bed tonight, reflect on the answers given today. May a sweet smile slide across your face as you thank God for revealing many of the distractions Satan is using in your life.

You are becoming "aware" of Satan's schemes and now have a plan to focus more on what the Bible says. Also, know that greater is He who is in you than he who is in the world (1 John 4:4). Keep focused on Jesus in the days to come.

Hebrews 12:1-3 (NIV) Therefore, since we are surrounded by such a great cloud of witnesses, let us throw off everything that hinders and the sin that so easily entangles, and let us run with perseverance the race marked out for us. Let us fix our eyes on Jesus, the author and perfecter of our faith, who for the joy set before him endured the cross, scorning its shame, and sat down at the right hand of the throne of God. Consider him who endured such opposition from sinful men, so that you will not grow weary and lose heart.

Ecclesiastes 7:10 Do not say, "Why were the old days better than these?" For it is not wise to ask such questions.

Theme word: **AVOID**

WEEK THREE
ONE QUESTION TO AVOID IN RELATIONSHIPS

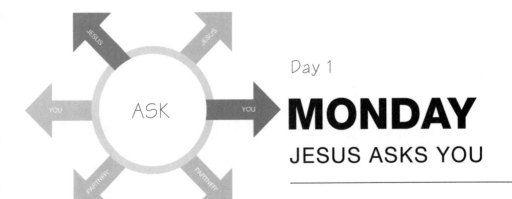

Day 1

MONDAY
JESUS ASKS YOU

When life is easy, we seem to ask few questions. When life is hard, we seem to have few answers. One thing is for certain, when life does get hard, we can default into asking God a lot of questions and one question that we want to avoid that will inevitably come up is the why question.

A why question typically passes judgment. Granted, a why question can work when we are simply obtaining information. Think about how a four-year-old uses the why question like a machine gun. Why is the sky blue? Why is the earth round? Why is the grass green? Why can't I have desert before dinner? However, even at such a young age, a better question may be formed with a how or what. How did the sky become blue? How does grass become green? What is the reason I can't eat candy all day long? How or what answers to these questions will elicit more information and steer clear of the judgmental tone.

The Bible gives us an example from the life of a man named Job. In the book of Job, Job asks God the why question sixteen times.[7] Job had lost his family, fortune and farm in a matter of moments. Many of us would be asking the same question.

> **Job 3:11 (NIV)** Why did I not perish at birth, and die as I came from the womb?

> **Job 10:2 (NASB)** I will say to God, 'Do not condemn me; Let me know why You contend with me.'

> **Job 21:4 (NIV)** Why should I not be impatient?

The interesting take away is that God never answers Job's why questions. As a matter of fact, God responds with sixty-four of His own questions. God begins by reminding Job who it is that created all things.

> **Job 38:1-4 (NIV)** Then the LORD answered Job out of the storm. He said: "Who is this that darkens my counsel with words without knowledge? Brace yourself like a man; I will question you, and you shall answer me. "Where were you when I laid the earth's foundation? Tell me, if you understand."

Now, keep in mind that Job's wife also lost her family, fortune and farm. She begins to speak foolishly, as we all can during times of intense stress. In one of the most loving rebukes, Job reminds her that they are in this together and corrects her theology with one simple question.

> **Job 2:10 (NASB)** But he said to her, "You speak as one of the foolish women speaks. Shall we indeed accept good from God and not accept adversity?" In all this Job did not sin with his lips.

You may be thinking, "Is it sinful to ask God the why question?" Be confident of this, God can handle any and all of our questions. He is God. We are not. However, we need to be careful with our motivation and the tone of this question when directed toward God, especially when we demand that He answers us.

I don't want to say the why question is completely wrong to use. There are many examples in the Bible where the why question is used in the Psalms and even in the Gospels. But it is almost always not the best question.

Learning to ask God the right questions during times of trial, testing and tribulation can ease some of the frustration during these times. Life is short and in our brief time here we need to learn to communicate with God in times of trouble and seek His help. Asking the right questions during these times can prove beneficial.

The Lord teaches some of His best lessons through trials. It is here we learn to trust Him, His words and His promises. During tough times we can doubt and question whether God is really in control. What happens next is that we may take the serpent at his word rather than trusting God at His.

Accepting good and adversity reminds us that God is continually teaching us through every circumstance and many times the answer to the why question is found in Romans 8:28-29.

> **Romans 8:28-29 (NASB)** And we know that God causes all things to work together for good to those who love God, to those who are called according to His purpose. For those whom He foreknew, He also predestined to become conformed to the image of His Son, so that He would be the firstborn among many brethren.

However, avoiding the why question in your relationship with God and with others will help you immensely, especially when you are going through trials. Read through James 1:2-5.

> **James 1:2-5 (NIV)** Consider it pure joy, my brothers, whenever you face trials of many kinds, because you know that the testing of your faith develops perseverance. Perseverance must finish its work so that you may be mature and complete, not lacking anything. If any of you lacks wisdom, he should ask God, who gives generously to all without finding fault, and it will be given to him.

How should we consider trials?

What will be developed?

When we lack wisdom, what should we do?

Sometimes what appears as though God were disappointing us, turns out to be God protecting us. Have you ever found this to be true after going through a trial?

In John 16:33, Jesus promises us that there is one thing that we will have for sure on this side of eternity. Write out Jesus' words from John 16:33 below.

Day 1

What is it that we can expect in this world and where is the place where we can find peace?

Sometimes we simply do not know what God is doing. But don't be discouraged. In the Gospels, the disciples frequently had no idea what Jesus was doing either, and they were roommates and traveling companions. On one occasion, Jesus washed their feet as He told them, "You do not realize now what I am doing, but later you will understand" (John 13:7). It is okay not to understand what God may be doing in your life. Perhaps later, you will.

If God asked you, "Shall you indeed accept good and not accept adversity?" How would you respond?

SUGGESTION
Write down your most frequently asked why question to God.

Some of life's greatest lessons are taught in the classroom of adversity. At the age of 28, I lost everything I had and went into depression trying to figure out why things were so tough in my life. The why question was probably one of my favorite as I directed it toward God and toward others. Things got even more frustrating as no one could give me a reason for why things were so difficult.

I, like Job, was doing everything I knew to please God. However, I was going through personal and professional trials that were quite painful. It was during this season that the Lord refined my faith and taught me about true riches through His eyes. He taught me about true worth being in my relationship with Him, not in what I had or what I owned. My theology was wrong and I needed correction. I was putting too much hope, security and identity in what I had instead of who I was, a child of God.

Three years afterwards, I wrote a book titled True Riches. The book focused on how to be rich in the eyes of God versus rich in the eyes of the world. I didn't really know what it meant to be rich until the Lord taught me. After going through this trial, I now embrace and am deeply comforted by this Psalm:

> **Psalm 119:71-72 (NIV)** It was good for me to be afflicted so that I might learn your decrees. The law from your mouth is more precious to me than thousands of pieces of silver and gold.

It has been said, "Pain is the touchstone of all spiritual progress."[8] May we welcome adversity and embrace the pain that brings us closer to God. The end result could be continued spiritual progress so we can also say, "It was good for me to be afflicted so that I might learn your decrees."

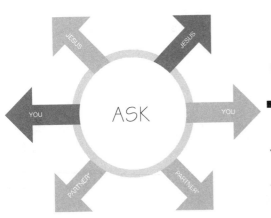

Day 2

TUESDAY
YOU ASK JESUS

Today is an invitation and an offer for you to converse with the Wonderful Counselor, Mighty God, Eternal Father, Prince of Peace (Isaiah 9:6), the Lord Jesus Christ. You may be in a sweet season of life right now or you may be in a tough one. If in a sweet season, thank Jesus. If you are in a difficult one, you may have no idea how things are going to work out. Yet, God continually gives us hope as we look to the Scriptures to teach us.

> **Romans 15:4 (NIV)** For everything that was written in the past was written to teach us, so that through endurance and the encouragement of the Scriptures we might have hope.

And God's word instructs us to "draw near to the throne of grace, so that we may receive mercy and find grace to help in the time of need" (Hebrews 4:16).

Read Hebrews 4:16. Where are we instructed to draw near?

What will we receive and what will we find?

When should we go before the throne of grace?

What five things do you ask God for the most?

1|

2|

3|

4|

5|

A study by a Christian research organization, The Barna Group, found that the top desires among Christians in the United States were: physical health, living with integrity, a marriage partner, living with a clear purpose and a close relationship with God.[9]

THE BIBLE DIRECTS US TO PRAY FOR ALL OF THESE REQUESTS:

1| For physical health: 3 John 2
2| For living with integrity: Proverbs 22:1, 1 Timothy 3:2, Titus 2:7
3| For a marriage partner: Proverbs 19:14, 20:6, 31:10
4| For living with a clear purpose: Colossians 1:9-10, Philippians 1:9-11
5| For a close relationship with God: Matthew 6:33, 11:28-30, Ephesians 1:17-18

Look up a few of the passages above and specifically ask for these things. Remember, the Lord is the source of all help (Psalm 121). If the Lord has answered these prayer requests, thank Him. If not, trust that He knows what is best for you. Proverbs 13:19 says, "A longing fulfilled is sweet to the soul." Answered prayer can be very sweet to the soul.

And if some of your prayers are not answered, do your best to avoid the why question and ask more what and how questions with the Lord. Remember God doesn't have to answer any of our why questions and we must be very careful when we use this question with Him and with others. Ask God to reveal areas where you are using the why question in a harsh manner.

HAVE YOU ASKED GOD ANY OF THESE WHY QUESTIONS? IF SO, CAN YOU REMEMBER WHEN?

Why are you allowing this to happen?   Y / N

Why don't you help me?   Y / N

Why won't you respond to my prayers?   Y / N

Why don't you get me out of this mess?   Y / N

As a reflective exercise, what were the last three why questions you remember asking? Were they directed toward God or toward another person? Was it done with a judgmental tone or to obtain information?

A relationship with the living God changes our life. He changes our desires. He changes our prayers. He even changes our questions. Yet, the one thing that never changes is Jesus for "Jesus Christ is the same yesterday and today and forever" (Hebrews 13:8).

SUGGESTION
Take time to read through the prayer below and be sure to confirm your meeting with your partner for tomorrow.

As your relationship with Jesus grows, ask Him to help you learn to develop a deeper trust in Him, not in circumstances. Sometimes the best prayer is asking God for peace even amid perplexing situations and seemingly unanswered prayers. Consider praying through the Serenity Prayer by Reinhold Niebuhr to gain perspective for today.

Day 2

God grant me the serenity
to accept the things I cannot change;
courage to change the things I can;
and wisdom to know the difference.

Living one day at a time;
Enjoying one moment at a time;
Accepting hardships as the pathway to peace;
Taking, as He did, this sinful world
as it is, not as I would have it;
Trusting that He will make all things right
if I surrender to His Will;
That I may be reasonably happy in this life
and supremely happy with Him
Forever in the next.
Amen.[10]

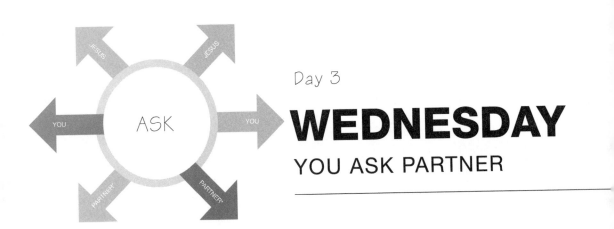

Day 3

WEDNESDAY

YOU ASK PARTNER

Learning to ask questions from the examples seen in the Scripture can be a whole new journey, especially when using the why question.

Avoiding the why question in your relationships will help you gather more information and steer clear of a judgmental tone. It is important that we look to follow examples from the pattern found in the Scriptures vs. the patterns found in this world.

> **Romans 12:2 (NIV)** Do not conform any longer to the pattern of this world, but be transformed by the renewing of your mind. Then you will be able to test and approve what God's will is--his good, pleasing and perfect will.

Paul instructs young Timothy to set an example in five different areas of life for other believers to follow. List the five areas where we are to be an example to others and next to each one, write the name of someone that has served as an example in that way for you.[11]

Read 1 Timothy 4:12 and write your answers below.

Area	Person that's been an example in your life	You as an example?
		Y / N / Not Yet
		Y / N / Not Yet
		Y / N / Not Yet
		Y / N / Not Yet
		Y / N / Not Yet

Which one best exemplifies you?

Which one do you need to work on the most?

Speech is the first item the Apostle Paul lists. Of all the ways God could have communicated to us, He chose words as the primary method.

Colossians 4:6 (NIV) Let your conversation be always full of grace, seasoned with salt, so that you may know how to answer everyone.

Think about how you use words and how you ask questions. Have you heard the saying, "Sticks and stones may break my bones but words will never hurt me"? This is not true. Words can hurt and words can heal. As you become more gracious with your words, you'll become more considerate with your questions.

PARTNER DISCUSSION:

1. Discuss at least one person in your life who is living out the example(s) you shared above. Briefly discuss how this has impacted your life? If you are able, contact this person this week and thank them for being an example of that attribute.

SUGGESTION
Consider quoting the passage in 1 Timothy 4:12 to the person you contact, they may appreciate you sharing Scripture with them. If no names are listed, pray and ask the Lord to bring people into your life who can help model these attributes for you.

2. Consider the usage, tone and directness of the following questions. Ask your partner:

Why are you wearing that?

Why aren't you more like Jesus?

Why were you late?

NOW, BEFORE THEY ANSWER CHANGE THE QUESTIONS TO:

How did you decide to wear that?

How can you become more like Jesus?

What caused you to be late?

WHICH QUESTIONS WOULD YOU PREFER TO ANSWER? DISCUSS.

Day 3

3. Ask your partner, what would you like me to do for you this week?

Your answer:

Partner's answer:

⊕ SUGGESTION
Think through and discuss how you and your partner
could ask more how and what questions.

Many people in the world pride themselves on incessantly asking the why question. For informational purposes this can be helpful. For personal, professional and spiritual relationships we should be careful and cautious. Using the why question with one another and especially with God needs to have a tender approach.

Christian writer, Thomas Merton said, "A person is known better by their questions than their answers." What will be the questions you will be known for asking?

Day 4

THURSDAY
YOU ASK YOU
Answering Jesus' Questions

When God uses the why question, He already knows the answer. He is the righteous judge, knowing the thoughts and intentions of our hearts (Hebrews 4:12). His judgment is perfect, precise and pure. Ours is not.

God's questions aren't intended to belittle us; they are intended to build us up. His questions are not intended to punish us; they are intended to powerfully remind us whom we are talking to. They do stir our mind; yet they should bend our knees while properly addressing the One who created and controls all things.

God can do whatever He pleases, He is God. Read these passages and share your thoughts below.

> **Psalm 115:3 (NASB)** But our God is in the heavens; He does whatever He pleases.

> **Psalm 135:6 (NASB)** Whatever the LORD pleases, He does, In heaven and in earth, in the seas and in all deeps.

> **Isaiah 45:7 (NIV)** I form the light and create darkness, I bring prosperity and create disaster; I, the LORD, do all these things.

Your thoughts?

The Lord is truly in control. When we don't understand what is happening in our life, we can put ourselves into the position of being God's advisor instead of being His servant. We need to be careful here. Sometimes, we can even start telling God what to do and He can remind us whom we are talking to. Remember God's response to Job with all of his why questions? Humbling isn't it?

> **Isaiah 40:21-23 (NIV)** Do you not know? Have you not heard? Has it not been told you from the beginning? Have you not understood since the earth was founded? He sits enthroned above the circle of the earth, and its people are like grasshoppers. He stretches out the heavens like a canopy, and spreads them out like a tent to live in. He brings princes to naught and reduces the rulers of this world to nothing.

> **Isaiah 40:13-15 (NASB)** Who has directed the Spirit of the LORD, Or as His counselor has informed Him? With whom did He consult and who gave Him understanding? And who taught Him in the path of justice and taught Him knowledge And informed Him of the way of understanding? Behold, the nations are like a drop from a bucket, And are regarded as a speck of dust on the scales; Behold, He lifts up the islands like fine dust.

When we are in a difficult season, our flesh and sinful nature will want to question God and ask Him if He knows what He is doing. Many times, we think to ourselves, "I would not orchestrate events like this. God must not be in control. Let me tell Him how I think He should handle this situation." Instead, the Lord asks us to trust Him even when things do not make sense in our mind or heart.

Have you ever had similar thoughts? Y / N

The why question for you and Jesus to discuss is one of His most penetrating. How would you answer Jesus if He were asking you this question directly? Write your response after the passage.

Luke 6:46 (NASB) Why do you call Me, 'Lord, Lord,' and do not do what I say?

TODAY THE EXERCISE IS SIMPLE TO EXPLAIN BUT DIFFICULT TO DO. HERE IS THE ASSIGNMENT:

See if you can go one day without complaining, starting now.

If you just read this assignment and complained about it, no problem, start again!

And if you do end up complaining, write down who or what it was that you complained about. Do your best to record this list on a notepad or electronic device today for discussion with your partner tomorrow. This is tougher than you might imagine. Be sure to keep a list.

Who or What was the complaint about	Explanation

⊕ SUGGESTION
Who will you most likely talk to the most today? Ask this person to take note of every time you complain and send the list via email or text before the end of the day to you. If possible, contact them right now and ask for their help. Be sure to keep your own list as well.

Day 4

Jesus' questions sober some, stun others and soothe many. When Jesus is using the why question, His judgment is perfect, pure and precise, as mentioned, ours is not. Is there a good reason for calling Jesus Lord and not doing what He says?

Also, do your best not to complain today. For many of us, this will be extremely difficult. We enjoy complaining about others, about our lives and even about what God has asked us to do. Have you ever noticed that many complaints begin with, "Why can't . . . why won't . . . why should . . . why does. . . "? Enjoy this simple yet difficult exercise.

Day 5

FRIDAY

SUMMARY & REFLECTION

Take a deep breath and a long exhale. I hope this week was difficult and delightful for you. Not complaining may have been difficult but delightful for those who spent time with you. And not using the why question may have also been difficult but delightful for those who were with you.

There are only a few questions today. You are entering the final week. May you finish well!

PERSONAL QUESTIONS:

1. Do you ever look at your life and ask, "What could God be teaching me through this?" What might be a reason the Lord has you going through this workbook in this season?

2. Today, begin a list of things you are thankful for. Write at least three items in each category. Share one or more items from each column when you meet. You are welcome to make the list longer if you wish.

People	Promises from God	Posessions

PARTNER DISCUSSION QUESTIONS:

1. What would your life look like if you obeyed this one command from Philippians 2:14-16?

Philippians 2:14-16 (NIV) Do everything without complaining or arguing, so that you may become blameless and pure, children of God without fault in a crooked and depraved generation, in which you shine like stars in the universe as you hold out the word of life--in order that I may boast on the day of Christ that I did not run or labor for nothing.

BONUS INSIGHT: Do you know where the Apostle Paul was when he wrote the book of Philippians? He was in a prison in Rome. He was not complaining. As a matter of fact, he was rejoicing. He was thanking God. He was praying for others. He was encouraging others to live with joy by giving thanks even in hard times. By doing this, Paul said that we would "shine likes stars."

2. Circle at least one item from each column on your thankful list and explain the reason you are thankful for that person, promise or possession with your partner.

3. Consider planning a celebration for your last meeting next week. Ideas?

SUGGESTION
Close today by confirming a place that you, your partner and / or group would enjoy meeting to conclude this study.

Do something fun. Eat something fantastic. Drink something fabulous. There will be a new set of questions to discuss at your last meeting. Taking time to refresh and encourage one another is a fantastic way to finish well. The Bible promises that, "A generous man will prosper; he who refreshes others will himself be refreshed" (Proverbs 11:25).

You have been through Jesus' most frequently asked question, the first question ever asked and one question to avoid in your relationship with God and with others. Great work!

I applaud you for your commitment and faithfulness to complete the assignments. By this time, you have had many conversations with Jesus and with others about Jesus and your relationships are deepening and developing.

As your understanding and skill develops with this one simple word – ask –may you truly experience your relationships growing beyond what you could have imagined.

> **Ephesians 3:20-21 (NIV)** Now to him who is able to do immeasurably more than all we ask or imagine, according to his power that is at work within us, to him be glory in the church and in Christ Jesus throughout all generations, for ever and ever! Amen.

The last week is focused on forever. Forever is an important word because, as you know, forever is a very long time. You may think this next chapter is one of those "of course, I know that" type chapters. It's not. This topic should move you to a greater depth, intimacy and understanding of Jesus and give you the opportunity to "shine like stars as you hold out the word of life" as this study concludes.

Finish strong, only 7 days left.

Day 5

Luke 10:25 (NIV) On one occasion an expert in the law stood up to test Jesus. "Teacher," he asked, "what must I do to inherit eternal life?"

Theme word: **FOREVER**

WEEKFOUR
ONE QUESTION EVEVERYONE MUST ANSWER

Day 1

MONDAY

What must I do to inherit eternal life?

Jesus was asked this question a number of times throughout Scripture. Some were asking to test Him, some were asking to inquire and some were asking because they really didn't know the answer.

> **Luke 10:25 (NIV)** On one occasion an expert in the law stood up to test Jesus. "Teacher," he asked, "what must I do to inherit eternal life?"

> **Luke 18:18 (NIV)** A certain ruler asked him, "Good teacher, what must I do to inherit eternal life?"

The answer to this question is extremely important. It has been asked by experts, rulers and will probably be asked by every one of us, "What must I do to inherit eternal life?" It is a great question to ask and a great question to answer from the Bible.

As you read through the Bible, you will find the Lord drawing all sorts of people into a relationship with Him. He seems to consistently use messed up ordinary people in extraordinary ways. And if you think your life is too messed up for God to use, consider this list of people from the Bible:

> Peter denied Christ.[12] Paul persecuted Christians.[13] Moses had a lack of confidence speaking.[14] Samson was a womanizer.[15] Rahab was a prostitute.[16] David committed adultery and was a murderer.[17] Elijah was depressed and suicidal.[18] Isaiah preached naked.[19] John the Baptist ate bugs.[20] The Samaritan woman was divorced five times and was living with her boyfriend.[21] Zaccheus was too small.[22] And Lazarus was dead[23] and God displayed His grace through each of them in wonderful ways.

God transforms all sorts of people. What is even more amazing is that Jesus continually welcomes a certain group. Read Luke 15:1-2 and write out what type of people Jesus welcomes.

JESUS WELCOMES:

Read Matthew 1:21. What will Jesus save people from?

Jesus invites all kinds of people to be with Him; however, every one of us must recognize and understand sin and what it means to be a sinner. In simple terms, sin is going against God by either disobeying His commands, doing something He prohibits or a rebellious attitude against Him. Sin is what separates us from a relationship with Him. The restoration for the relationship comes through God's grace which will lead us to repentance (Romans 2:4).

When John the Baptist began his ministry, he was given one primary message to share with others.

> **Matthew 3:1-2 (NASB)** Now in those days John the Baptist came, preaching in the wilderness of Judea, saying, "Repent, for the kingdom of heaven is at hand."

When Jesus began His ministry, His first words recorded in the Gospel of Mark were:

> **Mark 1:14-15 (NASB)** Jesus came into Galilee, preaching the gospel of God, and saying, "The time is fulfilled, and the kingdom of God is at hand; repent and believe in the gospel."

When Peter began his ministry in the book of Acts, Peter tells the people:

> **Acts 2:38 (NIV)** Peter replied, "Repent and be baptized, every one of you, in the name of Jesus Christ for the forgiveness of your sins. And you will receive the gift of the Holy Spirit.

What message did John the Baptist, Jesus and Peter all have in common when they began their ministry?

Christ Jesus came to save sinners. Former slave trader and writer of the song Amazing Grace, John Newton said, "I remember two things: that I am a great sinner, and that Christ is a great Savior."[24] And that's why grace and salvation are so amazing because we have nothing to offer God in exchange for our soul.

Sin is a three letter word that we don't like to discuss. However, for those who acknowledge sin, confess, repent and ask for forgiveness, the relationship with God is restored. Humbled sinners ask for help, knowing they cannot help themselves. Repentant sinners realize they deserve punishment; however, Jesus does not treat humbled and repentant sinners as their sins deserve but is merciful and forgives those who ask.

> **1 John 1:8-10 (NASB)** If we say that we have no sin, we are deceiving ourselves and the truth is not in us. If we confess our sins, He is faithful and righteous to forgive us our sins and to cleanse us from all unrighteousness. If we say that we have not sinned, we make Him a liar and His word is not in us.

Even the great Apostle Paul, in almost every message, would include words like this:

> **Acts 17:30 (NIV)** In the past God overlooked such ignorance, but now he commands all people everywhere to repent.

> **Acts 20:21 (NIV)** I have declared to both Jews and Greeks that they must turn to God in repentance and have faith in our Lord Jesus.

Our Holy God is mighty to save sinners. The best proof of that is when you consider He saved you.

> **Acts 4:12 (NIV)** Salvation is found in no one else, for there is no other name under heaven given to men by which we must be saved.

Day 1

Isaiah 63:1 (NIV) Our God is mighty to save.

Romans 3:23 (NIV) For all have sinned and fall short of the glory of God. Romans 6:23 (NIV) For the wages of sin is death, but the gift of God is eternal life in Christ Jesus our Lord.

When we are talking about the love of Jesus, we are talking about the deepest love in the world. We are talking about the One who saves us from our sin, hell and eternal separation from Him. By repenting and asking for forgiveness, Jesus has promised us eternal life. This is an amazing biblical love that would die for the one loved to make the relationship right. This is a love that lasts and endures forever. This is the love of Jesus.

The Bible gives assurance that nothing will ever separate you from the love of God that is in Christ Jesus our Lord (Romans 8:38). With that in mind, ask yourself these questions:

1. Jesus said, "I am the resurrection and the life. He who believes in Me will live, even though he dies; and whoever lives and believes in Me will never die. Do you believe this?" (John 11:25-26)

2. Jesus died for sinners. Does that describe you?[25] Y / N Explain.

TAKE SOME TIME AND REALLY THINK THROUGH YOUR ANSWERS.

Read through 1 John 5:11-15 before answering this last question: Have you asked Jesus for salvation and / or for the confidence to know you have been given eternal life? Y / N Briefly explain.

On a scale of 1 to 10 with 10 being the highest, how confident are you that you are saved from your sin and given eternal life with Jesus forever?

1   2   3   4   5   6   7   8   9   10

SUGGESTION
Come before Jesus to say a prayer of thanks for eternal life if you are confident you have it or say a prayer of repentance asking for eternal life if you are aware you do not. Acknowledge sin, repent and ask Jesus for forgiveness. This could be a question that profoundly impacts your life.

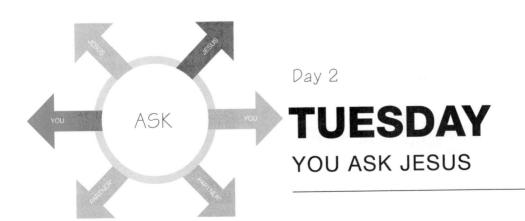

Day 2

TUESDAY

YOU ASK JESUS

We want things to last forever. As kids we may have signed notes BFF – best friends forever. Or we desire experiences with friends, food and fun to last forever. Yet, there are only three things designed to last for eternity.

Before I share those three things, is there one thing you wish would last forever? Have fun with your answer. There is no right or wrong answer here. Just enjoy using your imagination.
(I would answer pizza. I love pizza!)

1|

BIBLICALLY, THESE ARE THE ONLY THREE THINGS CREATED FOR ETERNITY:

1. God's Word.

Isaiah 40:8 (NASB) The grass withers, the flower fades, But the word of our God stands forever.

2. The souls of men and women.

Ecclesiastes 3:11, 14 (NIV) He has made everything beautiful in its time. He has also set eternity in the hearts of men; yet they cannot fathom what God has done from beginning to end. I know that everything God does will endure forever; nothing can be added to it and nothing taken from it. God does it so that men will revere him.

3. Love.

Jeremiah 31:3 (NIV) The LORD appeared to us in the past, saying: "I have loved you with an everlasting love; I have drawn you with loving-kindness."

We will experience a touch of forever upon our life as we align our lives with these three things. By embracing, engaging and enjoying these eternal truths, the Spirit of God comes alive in us.

Jesus has connected sinners, us, into eternal life with Him (Matthew 1:21-23). He became a mediator between us and God (1 Timothy 2:5) taking the appearance of a man (Philippians 2:8), He became Immanuel, which literally means "God with us." God with us and us with God joined together in perfect love forever and ever. What a relationship, gift and privilege for those who believe!

Great relationships are meant to last. Great relationships are based on God's word, a spiritual connection and love. Think of the greatest relationships in your life, you will probably find all three: God's word, God's eternal family and God's love brought together with a promise.

1 John 2:25 (NASB) This is the promise which He Himself made to us: eternal life.

The world says, "Promises are made to be _____." Yet, God is not like that. God always keeps His promises!

Within the eternal promise is the unique blessing of eternal rejoicing. Deep gratitude is what happens when someone gets "saved." When Jesus' disciples came to Him rejoicing that they had done many things in His Name; there was one specific thing He told them they should really be thankful for.

Read Luke 10:17-20 and write what Jesus tells His disciples to rejoice over from verse 20.

Look at the list you made last Friday, what is it that you are most thankful for on your list?

Was salvation listed? Y / N / How come it was or was not listed?

Salvation is one of, if not the most important topics of conversation you may ever have. Salvation is realizing you have been given the gift of eternal life to be with Jesus forever and ever and ever.

I asked my dad, "What is the most important thing in your life?" He answered, "Salvation. Salvation is the most important thing. As you get older, your faith is what counts. Cars and things can satisfy for a short time, but the only real thing that lasts is salvation."

When we are in love, we want to tell everybody about the person who has captured our heart. We also find people who are very much in love will talk more about the loved one than themselves. This becomes evidently true in our relationship with Jesus as well.

God showed His love for us by giving us His one and only Son. Life with the Son is the ultimate life, the abundant life, the life filled with joy unspeakable. Being saved from sin and being given everlasting life with Christ Jesus should have us filled with an inexpressible and glorious joy!

> **1 Peter 1:6-9 (NIV)** In this you greatly rejoice, though now for a little while you may have had to suffer grief in all kinds of trials. These have come so that your faith--of greater worth than gold, which perishes even though refined by fire--may be proved genuine and may result in praise, glory and honor when Jesus Christ is revealed. Though you have not seen him, you love him; and even though you do not see him now, you believe in him and are filled with an inexpressible and glorious joy, for you are receiving the goal of your faith, the salvation of your souls.

The Bible describes only two types of people, those who are saved and those who are lost. It is important to understand "lost people only matter to God; therefore, they should matter to us. Jesus came to seek and save the lost and has left us here, in part, to do the same. Our individual lives should reflect our obedience to tell others and to make disciples."[26]

> **Luke 19:10 (NASB)** "For the Son of Man has come to seek and to save that which was lost."

Day 2

At some point, everyone was lost and outside of God's Kingdom. God sent Jesus to save sinners by the power of the Holy Spirit. When God saves His people, He opens their eyes to love and to appreciate the supreme treasure that is Christ Jesus. "The gospel message—the news of Jesus' miraculous birth, perfect life, substitutionary death, and glorious resurrection—is great and joyous news."[27]

Keep reading through Luke 10:21-28. Write down the question asked in verse 25 and write your answer afterwards.

The question:

My answer:

If you are confident with your answer, great. If not, read through 2 Peter 1:10-11 and please discuss this with your partner tomorrow.

SUGGESTION

Confirm your meeting with your partner tomorrow and meditate on the things God says will last forever: His Word, your soul and His love. As you ponder these attributes, may you grasp and understand that your relationship with Jesus is to be enjoyed now and forever.

Deep gratitude flows from us to God as the One who gives life, breath and everything. We become immensely thankful as God's word, our soul and love come alive in a relationship with Jesus.

Zephaniah 3:17 (NIV) The LORD your God is with you, he is mighty to save. He will take great delight in you, he will quiet you with his love, he will rejoice over you with singing.

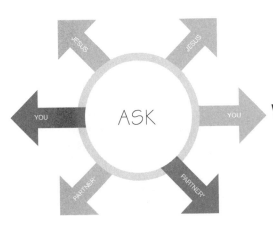

Day 3

WEDNESDAY

YOU ASK PARTNER

CONVERSATIONS WITH JESUS AND ABOUT JESUS CHANGE LIVES.

> **Philippians 2:9-11 (NASB)** For this reason also, God highly exalted Him, and bestowed on Him the name which is above every name, so that at the name of Jesus EVERY KNEE WILL BOW, of those who are in heaven and on earth and under the earth, and that every tongue will confess that Jesus Christ is Lord, to the glory of God the Father.

Write out 2 Corinthians 5:20.

The Bible says we are God's ambassadors, as though God were making His appeal through us to plead with others to be reconciled to God. Can you identify a person God has used as an ambassador in your life who has encouraged you to follow Jesus? How did the message they shared impact you?

AS AMBASSADORS OF GOD, WE HAVE INSTRUCTIONS TO DO TWO MAIN THINGS:

1. To go and tell others about Jesus.

> **Matthew 28:10 (NIV)** Then Jesus said to them, "Do not be afraid. Go and tell . . ."

2. To make disciples by teaching others to observe the commands of God.

> **Matthew 28:19-20 (NASB)** "Go therefore and make disciples of all the nations, baptizing them in the name of the Father and the Son and the Holy Spirit, teaching them to observe all that I commanded you; and lo, I am with you always, even to the end of the age."

We are to reflect God's light shining into a dark world. If light isn't seen and darkness grows, what is to be said about the light? It is either being hidden or concealed.

> **2 Corinthians 4:5-6 (NIV)** For we do not preach ourselves, but Jesus Christ as Lord, and ourselves as your servants for Jesus' sake. For God, who said, "Let light shine out of darkness," made his light shine in our hearts to give us the light of the knowledge of the glory of God in the face of Christ.

> **Matthew 5:14-16 (NASB)** "You are the light of the world. A city set on a hill cannot be hidden; nor does anyone light a lamp and put it under a basket, but on the lampstand, and it gives light to all who are in the house. "Let your light shine before men in such a way that they may see your good works, and glorify your Father who is in heaven."

> **John 8:12 (NIV)** When Jesus spoke again to the people, he said, "I am the light of the world. Whoever follows me will never walk in darkness, but will have the light of life."

Read 1 Peter 2:9. These passages explain who you are and what you are to do.

> **1 Peter 2:9 (NIV)** But you are a chosen people, a royal priesthood, a holy nation, a people belonging to God, that you may declare the praises of him who called you out of darkness into his wonderful light.

You are a _____ people, a royal _____, a
_____ nation, a people _____ to God, that you
may _____ the praises of Him who called you out of darkness into
His wonderful _____.

Circle and meditate on at least one word from above. Reflect on who the Bible says you are.

PARTNER DISCUSSION SECTION:

1. When you were younger, did you sing, "This little light of mine, I'm going to let it shine. This little light of mine, I'm going to let it shine. Let it shine, let it shine, let it shine"?

_____ Yes _____ No
_____ I have no clue about this song.
_____ I will not be able to get this song out of my head for the rest of the day.

We are given the opportunity to "shine like stars in the universe" as we hold out the words of life (Philippians 2:14-16) in a dark world. And Jesus invites us to "let your light shine before others, so that they may see your good works and give glory to your Father who is in heaven" (Matthew 5:16).

How have you seen or are you seeing the light of Christ shine through your partner? Explain.

2. Share your story of faith in Jesus and how your life has changed since this relationship began. Be brief. Take about 2-5 minutes. You can share more in your time together at the end of the week.

3. Ask your partner, what would you like me to do for you this week?

Your answer:

Partner's answer:

These next questions can be a bit personal. You can choose whether you and your partner would like to discuss them or not. If so, great. If not, do not feel any pressure or obligation to do so. Many of your answers may be "no one" or "I am not" or "I have not been doing that." If you are being honest, you are being authentic and real and just having these next conversations could really impact your life and the lives of many.

Day 3

As we follow the words from God, we will talk about them. When we really believe God's word is important, we will REALLY talk about it. Sharing the story of Jesus becomes a blessing, not a burden.

4. When was the last time you had a spiritual conversation with someone about Jesus?

5. Is there someone God has brought into your life that you have wanted to have a conversation about Jesus but have been scared to or the time just hasn't seemed right? What is his / her name?

The Apostle Paul's life was changed by the love of God. He went from being a persecutor of Christ (Acts 9:4) to a fully devoted follower of Jesus. With this change, he loved people so much that he shared with them the gospel of God and he invited them into his life as well.

> **1 Thessalonians 2:8 (NIV)** We loved you so much that we were delighted to share with you not only the gospel of God but our lives as well, because you had become so dear to us.

When we are moved by the love of Jesus, we will do that which He has commanded us to do (James 2:17). Letting people into our life opens the door for the privilege of telling them about Jesus. And making disciples teaching them to observe the commands of God directly involves letting people into our life as well.

SUGGESTION
Begin praying for the person listed above in question five. Prayerfully consider inviting him / her into a conversation and ask one of these questions:

- Do you ever think about spiritual things?
- Has anyone ever taken the time to explain to you how a personal relationship with Jesus is possible?[28]
- How would you respond if I asked you, "What must I do to inherit eternal life?"

If they do not have a biblical answer, ask them if they would like to know how the Bible answers these questions. If the conversation continues, ask them if they know what Jesus' most frequently asked question was? If not, consider inviting them to do this workbook with you.

Conversations with Jesus and about Jesus change lives. Someone had a conversation with you about salvation and there may be a few people whom the Lord has prepared for you to do the same. Be mindful that before you talk to a person about God, talk to God about that person.

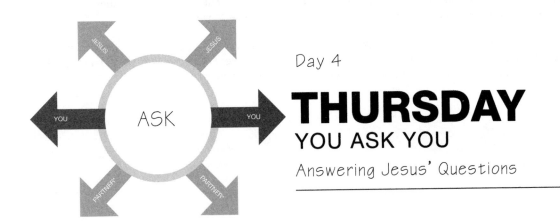

Day 4

THURSDAY
YOU ASK YOU
Answering Jesus' Questions

Satan does not want you talking about Jesus. Many times we can become really scared about talking with someone about Jesus. We may be fearful about what they will think of us, how they will react, and if they will ever want to talk to us again. All sorts of fears come up. Furthermore, Satan does not like us talking about sin and how to please God instead of continually looking to please ourselves.

Isaiah 59:1-2 (NIV) Surely the arm of the LORD is not too short to save, nor his ear too dull to hear. But your iniquities have separated you from your God; your sins have hidden his face from you, so that he will not hear.

Acts 3:19-21 (NIV) Repent, then, and turn to God, so that your sins may be wiped out, that times of refreshing may come from the Lord, and that he may send the Christ, who has been appointed for you--even Jesus. He must remain in heaven until the time comes for God to restore everything, as he promised long ago through his holy prophets.

1 John 1:9 (NIV) If we confess our sins, he is faithful and just and will forgive us our sins and purify us from all unrighteousness.

As the Apostle Paul matured in his faith and grew in his relationship with God, he didn't really care what others thought of him. He was more concerned with pleasing God above anything else.

Galatians 1:10 (NIV) Am I now trying to win the approval of men, or of God? Or am I trying to please men? If I were still trying to please men, I would not be a servant of Christ.

Over time, Paul's description of himself changed. It began with:

"Least of the apostles" – A.D. 55

1 Corinthians 15:9-10 (NIV) For I am the least of the apostles and do not even deserve to be called an apostle, because I persecuted the church of God. But by the grace of God I am what I am, and his grace to me was not without effect. No, I worked harder than all of them--yet not I, but the grace of God that was with me.

About seven years later . . .

"Least of all God's people"

Ephesians 3:8 (NIV) Although I am less than the least of all God's people, this grace was given me: to preach to the Gentiles the unsearchable riches of Christ.

About five years after that. . .

"The worst sinner"

1 Timothy 1:15 (NIV) Here is a trustworthy saying that deserves full acceptance: Christ Jesus came into the world to save sinners--of whom I am the worst.

As we mature in our faith, we should become more aware of our sinful condition. We should also recognize how the grace of God has lavishly been poured upon our life. This grace continually leads us to repentance and restores us into a right relationship with the Lord.

Romans 2:4 (NASB) Or do you think lightly of the riches of His kindness and tolerance and patience, not knowing that the kindness of God leads you to repentance?

Ephesians 2:8-9 (NIV) For it is by grace you have been saved, through faith--and this not from yourselves, it is the gift of God-- not by works, so that no one can boast.

We need to be mindful that we do not earn salvation. It is a gift given by God. For those who have received this gift, it is a privilege to tell others about Jesus. Jesus not only forgives sinners, but welcomes them and grants eternal life to those who repent and ask to be saved. This is a message for all to hear.

2 Corinthians 4:5 (NIV) For we do not preach ourselves, but Jesus Christ as Lord, and ourselves as your servants for Jesus' sake.

Romans 10:17 (NIV) Faith comes from hearing the message, and the message is heard through the word of Christ.

At some point, God sent a person into your life to tell you about Jesus. Do you remember his / her name? How and when did this occur?

Their name:

How and when did you receive this message?

Have you ever thanked this person for being an ambassador for the gospel? Y / N

If they are alive today, do your best to contact them and tell them thank you. If they are not alive, consider writing a note or calling a next of kin family member to let them know how God used this person to share the love of Christ in your life.

The person listed was someone in love with Jesus and loved you enough to tell you the truth of how He saves sinners. The story of Jesus is the greatest story ever told and greatest message ever heard. What a privilege to have someone share that with you and for you to share that with others.

Prayerfully consider having a conversation with at least one person whom God has brought into your life. Perhaps the Lord will use you as the ambassador to give a hopeful message in the same way someone did that for you. This could be a life-changing conversation with eternal significance.

As a comforting thought, the great preacher David Martyn Lloyd-Jones wrote about foundational principles for evangelism. Here are his top two principles to consider:

1| The supreme object of the work of evangelism is to glorify God, not to save souls.
2| The only power that can do this is the Holy Spirit, not our own strength.[29]

Day 4

This week, invite someone you have been praying for into a
conversation about Jesus.

I will invite _____ to join me for coffee / lunch / dinner / a walk. In this moment,
I pray for him / her and ask the Lord to divinely guide our conversation about Him.

Lord Jesus, please give me the courage and compassion to be an ambassador for this eternally
important conversation. Amen.

FRIDAY

SUMMARY & REFLECTION

PERSONAL DISCUSSION QUESTIONS:

1. Is salvation a difficult or delightful topic for you to discuss?

Explain what you think is the reason you answered the way you did.

2. What insight did you gain from each chapter? After answering, circle which chapter was your favorite.

Week #1: Jesus' Most Frequently Asked Question

Week #2: The First Question Ever Asked

Week #3: One Question to Avoid in Relationships

Week #4: One Question Everyone Must Answer

3. After investing four weeks in this study:

What is one thing you need to start doing?

What is one thing you need to stop doing?

What is one thing you need to keep doing?

PARTNER DISCUSSION QUESTIONS:

1. What did you learn about Jesus that was insightful and / or life-changing over the last four weeks?

2. What did you learn about yourself that was insightful and / or life-changing?

3. Read Ecclesiastes 4:9. What were the benefits from having a partner in this study? Be specific and share at least two things you learned or appreciated about your partner; however, feel free to add more.

4. Disciples of Jesus are commanded to do two things: 1) To tell others about Him 2) To make disciples teaching them to observe the commands of God. Is this something you are doing or plan to do? Is this something you look forward to doing or is this something you dread? Explain.

Day 5
_____

5. Is there another person you would like to do this workbook with? Who and how come?

6. Has your ability to ask questions improved or changed based on the examples learned from the Scriptures? Specifically, how will you begin applying those changes in your life beginning today?

7. Ask your partner one last question. Before today ends, "What is one thing that you would like me to do for you?"

YOU HAVE BEEN ON A FOUR-WEEK JOURNEY DESIGNED TO HELP YOU DO TWO THINGS:

1| Talk with Jesus.
2| Talk with others about Jesus using one simple word.

Well done. Now may you celebrate with your partner!

The Bible is the greatest story ever told and the greatest book ever written. Perhaps it is because it holds the greatest love story ever shared? Souls are saved. People are rescued. Hope for the hopeless is given. And the promise of a loving relationship that will last forever is extended. It's the story of Jesus. It's the story of the greatest servant, the greatest helper, the greatest source of love giving us the promise to be in a relationship with Him forever and ever. It's a take your breath away story.

Jesus is the Alpha and the Omega. He is the beginning and the end of everything. He is who was, who is, and who is to come. He is the Almighty (Revelation 1:8 NAS). He is the living Word. He is everlasting life and He is eternal love. He is who we will be talking with and about forever!

All things have been created through Him and for Him and we have such a unique privilege to be in a relationship with Him to be enjoyed now and for eternity.

> **Colossians 1:16-18 (NIV)** For by him all things were created: things in heaven and on earth, visible and invisible, whether thrones or powers or rulers or authorities; all things were created by him and for him. He is before all things, and in him all things hold together. And he is the head of the body, the church; he is the beginning and the firstborn from among the dead, so that in everything he might have the supremacy.

As you spend more time with Jesus, may you be captivated by His questions, His answers, His love, His gentleness, His kindness and His eternal wisdom. May there be a new confidence, change and courage that flow from being with Him and meditating on His words.

People are generally impressed with academic degrees, physical beauty, professional positions and worldly belongings. These things do not matter much compared to the surpassing greatness of knowing Christ Jesus as Lord and Savior (Philippians 3:8). May people truly be astonished and recognize you as someone who has "been with Jesus" and may His light shine through you as an ordinary person loved by an extraordinary God.

> **Acts 4:13 (NIV)** When they saw the courage of Peter and John and realized that they were unschooled, ordinary men, they were astonished and they took note that these men had been with Jesus.

Serve the Lord and others sincerely. Share His words. Be aware of Satan's schemes and avoid asking why. And know this, God has even better things in store for those who have been promised eternal life.

> **Hebrews 6:9 (NIV)** Even though we speak like this, dear friends, we are confident of better things in your case--things that accompany salvation.

May one simple word—ask—help deepen and develop many of the relationships in your life, first with Jesus and then with others. The grace of the Lord Jesus be with you all. Amen.[30]

CLOSING

Professionally, Todd Sinelli has worked in the financial markets managing hedge funds and trading at the Chicago Board Options Exchange (CBOE). He has served as the director of international expansion for a franchise company and has been a professional magician, missionary in Italy, director of counseling for a mega-church and has authored four books.

Todd holds a BBA from Michigan State University, an MBA from the University of Dallas and has studied at The Wharton School's Executive Education Program. He is a certified biblical counselor through the National Association of Nouthetic Counselors (NANC) and his current passion is teaching others how to have relationships at their best through the power of one simple word.

Todd has served as an advocate and spokesperson for Compassion International and has partnered with several Christian organizations and conferences in the United States and abroad.

Personally, he enjoys tennis, travel and all things Italian. He has lived in Detroit, Chicago, Northern California, Nantucket, Italy and currently lives in Dallas, Texas. Todd can be contacted through littorch.com.

ABOUT LIT TORCH PUBLISHING:

Lit Torch Publishing was created to reflect the light of Christ through everything we do. We pray that with every publication and presentation two things occur: One is that people learn something new and two is that they are excited to share that knowledge with others.

You are invited to visit littorch.com to ask and to answer a few questions. Plus, you will find articles and opportunities to learn how to become an ambassador for the OSW project. We look forward to serving you.

ABOUT THE AUTHOR

If you are walking along and see a turtle sitting on a fence post, one thing you know for sure is it did not get there by itself. This is my story as well. This workbook was shaped, molded and refined by many wonderful people in my life. This section is similar to the Apostle Paul writing Romans chapter 16 with so many people to thank. All of you have helped place this turtle on the fence post. Thank you!

Dad & Kim: First supporters, first beta group, first Kickstarter contributors, thank you. So, great to have your encouragement and participation along the way. Mom: You've modeled a curious spirit and continual desire to learn. Thank you for teaching me the importance of God and going to church at a young age. The significance of those two things shapes me daily. Dallas beta group: Andrew Lewis: Thanks for keeping me focused upon each day. I stand up and applaud the growth and transformation that has occurred in your life over the last few years. Your questions are changing the lives of many, keep asking. Jennifer Bush (soon to be Jennifer Lewis): You and Andrew are a great team. You both continually presented subtle, yet significant suggestions. Thank you. Jarrod Pitts: Using only what is necessary. Keeping things tight and brief from a logical engineering perspective helped tremendously. Elizabeth Mayfield: Your consistent walk with the Lord inspired us all. Joe Epperson: Keep being a Berean and embracing God's word as it is, the very words of God. A delight watching you grow. Jack Thurman: You are one of a kind. Your drawing of Satan will linger in my mind for many days. Thanks for welcoming all the challenges that I've presented to you. Your growth is evident among those who are paying close attention. Alexandra Rearick: Artistic style and a love for God's Word make you a powerful contributor. Your honesty and touch upon this project have been timely, divine and professionally polished. Your best days are yet ahead of you. Elizabeth Dressen: Jumping in, learning, asking and watching you interact with the material and the beta group refined many points. Thank you. Lukas Moffett: Having you there by facetime and in person was part of the grand finale and learning that your most frequently asked question soon became, "Who wants to hear 1 Corinthians 13?" and "Has anyone seen my finger sleeve?" puts a smile on my face. Monica Foote: Your New York boldness, panache and love for the Lord continually helped move this project in the right direction. Thank you for being you. Colin Lardner: Boom! Your conversations, collaborations and continual Christ-centered core is what I like best about you. Thanks for supporting this project and adding your insight, intrigue and inquisitiveness. Looking forward to partnering in more ministry projects in the near future. Rob Heath: I think you are a diamond shining among us. Your style, stylist and sweet soul helped shape this project, thank you. Jeff Blem: When you were with us, you reaffirmed the good and had us think on ways to improve the not so good. Thanks. Angelo Kolettis: There he is! What a journey these last few years have been for both of us. Your best days are yet ahead of you and looking forward to developing some projects and platforms to share your gifts in Italia and across the globe. 360 Optimal Fitness has really helped me become stronger physically, mentally and spiritually. Thank you for serving me as a friend and professional. Kevin Ainsworth: Thank you for being a wise friend and for providing a place to have solace, rest and to host others. My life is richer because of you. Kim Truman: Thank you for giving the encouragement to share my gifts and for providing Adrenaline. You make fitness and life fun. Keep the turtle spirit alive. Bobby Crotty: As you mentioned, great writing is in removing, not adding. Thanks for helping make this workbook great. Joe Daly: You are becoming the most compassionate and patient guy I know. Thanks for coming on board and for being part of this "tidal wave." Bill & Lee Mancini: Any friend of Tom & Deb Steipp is a friend of mine, especially someone teaching the 5 Aspects of Woman class! Thank you for launching the beta group in Knoxville.

ACKNOWLEDGEMENTS

Your insight and feedback with the group has shaped this document significantly. Let's pray for more lives to be changed from this teaching with action and application as the result. To all the Kickstarter supporters, it worked. The OSWW has been kick started. Now, the adventure begins. Thank you deeply and dearly for supporting this from the beginning. Rebecca Roundtree: Fantastic editing. Your prayers, contribution, and encouragement have helped infuse divine power into this project. Thank you for serving the Lord and me through your giftedness. Paul and Jen Legge: Superb friends. Superb servants. Superb superstars in my world. Thank you for being there with honest feedback, generous support and warm hospitality. I love being a part of your family and watching everyone grow through test, trials and triumphs. Let's keep doing "exactly" what our Lord asks us. Levi and Suzanne Nunnick: I'm letting the secret out, a web savvy technological savant with the coding skills of modern day rain man and the mind of GK Chesterton helped with the web platform while a super godly wife with six kids, the wisdom of Elizabeth Elliot and seamstress ability of Coco Chanel worked on the finger sleeve. Thanks for dreaming and working on these projects with me. Watermark Church: May it be said that we do biblical community that is worth modeling. May we continue to ask people to, "Come and see, not our church, but our Savior." Todd Wagner, Kyle Thompson, Rick Wisner, Blake Holmes, Bobby Rodriguez, thank you for allowing me to serve alongside of you in Dallas. Dr. Rick Thomas: You planted the seed. May this workbook continue to yield fruit from the rifle, shotgun, x-ray and seemingly infinite number of questions you tested me on pertaining to theology and counseling. Thank you for being a teacher in my life. Mike & Nanci Perkaus: Your home, discussions, prayer and constant friendship has kept us together and will keep us together serving our Lord and one another. So glad Carmel became my quiet supporter and was pivotal for clarifying the final pages of this project. Thank you for being with me at the beginning and praying faithfully toward its completion. You both rock! James Bibbings: The greatest joy of a teacher is to be surpassed by his pupils. I see you surpassing me in the days ahead. Keep teaching and sharing your gift with others. May Amanda be your best and favorite disciple and beware of any theologian that uses the word - unforgiveness. Jim, Deanna and Catherine Achilles: Your encouragement and gentleness in refining this workbook were a great help. Yet, seriously, how come you didn't get at least one wrong from that quiz? Robb Besosa: Enjoying Soup and nuts, white knuckles, pizza, pet rocks, and "Remembering One" poem while your kids quote Brian Regan lines will be forever remembered. Thank you for being a friend, counselor and role model in my life. Scott O'Malley: Love your passion for the Word and your love for the world's greatest payment processor. Having you on the team helps ensure that there will be no proof texting nor sloppy theology. Thanks for grooming through this workbook. Always a pleasure being with you and your family. Craig Mercer: Every time I am with you, I learn so much. Love your insight into Satan and the human condition. Appreciate you sharing your perspective in a sweet and sincere manner. Scott Faulkner: Ah, the dream relationship, a life without questions. And why is the author asking so many questions? Jim McClarty: You really are a stickler for sound doctrine. Thanks for poking me with that stick. All for Him. Sajit Sasi: You've made it into almost every book of mine, well done. Thanks for being a biblical friend and devoted follower of Jesus. You're a gift from God in my life. Stinson & Sudha Mathai: The godliest couple in all of Texas. Thank you for sharing your photography magic, your golfing talents and your godly generosity with me. Todd Martincello: Being in Hawaii, being refreshed and being reset with you at the Pipe Masters was so timely. I think this is your year when many longings become fulfilled and sweet to the soul. Thanks for being a great friend and fellow ambassador to serve our Lord. Jeff Dunn: Less is more. Thank you for the last minute edits with Allie. The Indian Bullet bread and Tikka Masala were the missing ingredients to spice everything up. Bob Toyama: Your prayers helped shaped the closing and meet the timeline. Thank you. Allen Hankins and Brandon Avance: Thanks for being the first with the finished product. You are social media gurus. Eager to partner in ministry and may we continue to disciple many men across the nation. And to Jesus, without You there is no me. Thank you for preparing this good work in advance for me to do (Ephesians 2:10).

[1] John Dear, *The Questions of Jesus*, (New York, NY: Doubleday, 2004), 9-10.

[2] Tom J. Cowley, *A Biography of Jesus* (Tiburon, CA: Eagle's Nest Press, 2005), 36.

[3] Scott Witt, *How to Be Twice as Smart* (New York, NY; Penguin Putnam, 1983), 129.

[4] *The Briefing Book*, http://www.911dispatch.com/info/fact_figures.html

[5] C.S. Lewis, *They Joyful Christian* (New York, NY; Simon & Schuster, 1977), 141.

[6] Answer: Divine. Alexander Pope, Essay on Criticism, 1709. Retrieved from http://dictionary.reference.com/browse/to+err+is+human,+to+forgive+divine

[7] Don Baker, *Pain's Hidden Purpose* (Portland, OR: Multnomah Press, 1984), 103.

[8] Alcoholics Anonymous, *Twelve Steps and Twelve Traditions* (New York, NY: Alcoholics Anonymous World Services, Inc., 1952), 93.

[9] The Barna Group, *Survey Details Current Vision of the American Dream*, June 23, 2008.

[10] Reinhold Niebuhr, *Serenity Prayer*, Retrieved January 5, 2013 from http://en.wikipedia.org/wiki/Serenity_Prayer

[11] Henry & Tom Blackaby, *The Man God Uses* (Nashville, TN: Lifeway Press, 1998), 49.

[12] Mark 14:66-72.

[13] Acts 8:3.

[14] Exodus 6:12, 30.

[15] Judges 14:1-3; 16:1-2.

[16] Joshua 6:25.

[17] 2 Samuel 11.

[18] 1 Kings 19:1-4.

[19] Isaiah 20:2.

[20] Matthew 3:4.

[21] John 4:16-18.

[22] Luke 19:3-6.

[23] John 11:32-46.

[24] Chris Tiegreen, *One Year Walk with God Devotional* (Wheaton, IL: Tyndale House, 2004), September 25.

[25] Will Metzger, *Tell the Truth* (Downers Grove, IL: Intervarsity Press, 2002), 80.

[26] Watermark Community Church Values. Retrieved on January 20, 2013 from http://www.watermark.org/about-us/values/

[27] Tim Challies, *The Discipline of Spiritual Discernment* (Wheaton, IL: Crossway Books, 2007), 31-32.

[28] Randy Newman, *Questioning Evangelism* (Grand Rapids, MI: Kregel Publicaltions, 2004), 242.

[29] D. Martyn Lloyd-Jones, *The Presentation of the Gospel* (Downer's Grove, IL: IntervVarsity Press, 1949). 6-7.

[30] Revelation 22:21.

END NOTES